GREBES
OF THE WORLD

GREBES
OF THE WORLD

TEXT MALCOLM OGILVIE
PAINTINGS CHRIS ROSE

BRUCE COLEMAN

First published in 2003 by
Bruce Coleman
16 Chiltern Business Village
Arundel Road
Uxbridge, UB8 2SN

Distributed by
NHBS Ltd
2–4 Wills Road
Totnes
Devon TQ9 5XN

British Library Cataloguing-in-Publication Data
A catalogue record for this book is available from the British Library.

ISBN 1 872842 03 8

Typefaces used: Hoefler Text (main text); Bembo (headings).

Edited and designed by
D & N Publishing
Baydon, Marlborough, Wiltshire.

Printed and bound in Italy by Eurografica S.P.A.

CONTENTS

ACKNOWLEDGEMENTS

MALCOLM OGILVIE THANKS ROBERT DICKERMAN AND Lucienne Wilme for their help with the names of grebes.

For their invaluable help in providing reference material for many of the less well-known species, Chris Rose would like to thank David Allen, John Cox, Barry Van Dusen, Simon Harrap, Dr Mike Harris, Jon Fjeldså, Dr Xavier Ferrer, David Willard, Birdlife International (Library) and the staff and facilities of the Bird Group, The Natural History Museum, Tring. Without their assistance, some of the paintings in this book could not have been produced.

Bruce Coleman thanks David and Namrita Price-Goodfellow (D & N Publishing) for their essential production and editorial expertise. Mark Balman, of the splendid Birdlife International kindly did the maps, while Rachel Coleman and Alison Duffy came to Bruce's aid rather more frequently than he can remember.

INTRODUCTION TO THE GREBES

EVOLUTION

The family of grebes is one of the oldest in the world. Recognizable grebes have been found among fossils from 80 million years ago. The first specimens attributable to *Podiceps*, one of the six present-day genera, date back at least 25 million years. All the grebes are placed in the single family, the Podicipedidae, which, in turn, is the sole family in the order Podicipediformes. Grebes appear to have few close relatives. The former grouping with the divers, which was based mainly on their appearance and general aquatic habits, has not withstood the test of modern techniques of taxonomic research. It seems more likely that this is an example of convergent evolution: some superficial similarities appeared because the birds shared some of their habitat and lifestyle characteristics. The latest thinking is that the grebes have evolved from a common ancestor which produced not only them, but also the penguins, herons, storks, petrels and other seabirds such as boobies, pelicans and cormorants. Much of the evolution of the grebes appears to have taken place in what is now South America and today there is still a major concentration of species there.

TAXONOMY

Just as the birds themselves have evolved over time, so their taxonomy has changed as different ideas have been put forward on the divisions into genera, species and subspecies. Some of these become widely accepted, others are debated and modified, yet others fall by the wayside. For the purposes of this book, the classification of Morony, Bock and Farrand (1975) has been adopted. This is the system followed in many major books on birds, including the magisterial *Handbook of the Birds of the World* (del Hoyo *et al.* 1992). Accordingly, the grebes are divided into six genera, *Tachybaptus, Podilymbus, Rollandia, Poliocephalus, Podiceps* and *Aechmophorus*. They are further separated into 22 species and a further 31 subspecies.

TACHYBAPTUS

This genus contains five species, one widespread in Eurasia and Africa, one in Australasia, two confined to the island of Madagascar, and one in South America. The first four are undoubtedly closely related, and some hybridization has occurred between three of them.

LITTLE GREBE *TACHYBAPTUS RUFICOLLIS*
Divided into nine subspecies in a range which stretches from western Europe to south-east Asia and throughout sub-Saharan Africa.

AUSTRALASIAN GREBE *TACHYBAPTUS NOVAEHOLLANDIAE*
Seven subspecies occur in Indonesia (some of them confined to single islands) and in Australia and New Zealand. As recently as the 1940s, an overlap in range with Little Grebe, without apparent hybridization, was accepted as evidence that this was a separate species and not a subspecies of Little Grebe.

MADAGASCAR GREBE *TACHYBAPTUS PELZELNII*
Monotypic. Confined to the island of Madagascar and known to have hybridized with Little Grebe.

ALAOTRA (OR RUSTY) GREBE *TACHYBAPTUS RUFOLAVATUS*
Confined to a very small area of Madagascar where it is now probably extinct. Sharply declining numbers have been hybridizing with increasing numbers of Little Grebe, and no pure birds have been seen for about ten years.

LEAST GREBE *TACHYBAPTUS DOMINICUS*
Four subspecies occur within the Central and South American range. This species lacks any of the chestnut found on the neck of the other four species in the genus. Past taxonomic proposals have placed it in at least two other current genera as well as in one on its own in

recognition of the considerable geographical separation from the rest of the genus.

PODILYMBUS

There are just two species in this genus, both confined to the New World. One is now extinct. They clearly stem from a common stock. The Atitlán Grebe probably became isolated at some time in the distant past after which it evolved into a larger, flightless subspecies.

PIED-BILLED GREBE *PODILYMBUS PODICEPS*

This widespread bird occurs from temperate North America to the southern tip of South America. Three subspecies have been described.

ATITLÁN GREBE *PODILYMBUS GIGAS*

Confined to a single lake in Guatemala, this monotypic and flightless species became extinct in the 1980s, firstly through major changes to its habitat and food availability, and secondly through probable hybridization with the Pied-billed Grebe.

ROLLANDIA

Two species occur, both in South America. One is widespread, the other flightless and found only in one small area. Both were formerly placed in *Podiceps*, but separate genera have also been proposed.

WHITE-TUFTED GREBE
ROLLANDIA ROLLAND

Three subspecies occupy the range of the southern half of South America, including the Falkland Islands. The latter has been suggested as a separate species.

TITICACA FLIGHTLESS GREBE
ROLLANDIA MICROPTERA

This monotypic and flightless grebe occurs on Lake Titicaca and a handful of connected lakes.

POLIOCEPHALUS

Two species are placed in this genus, one Australian, the other in New Zealand. Both are fairly obviously derived from a common ancestor, but the two have been geographically separated for a long time. The recent colonization of New Zealand's South Island by the Australian species will be watched with interest to see if it leads to a spread into the range of the other species, found only on North Island.

HOARY-HEADED GREBE
POLIOCEPHALUS POLIOCEPHALUS

Monotypic. This species is found widely in suitable areas of Australia and Tasmania. One or two pairs bred in New Zealand in the 1970s and perhaps since.

NEW ZEALAND GREBE
POLIOCEPHALUS RUFOPECTUS

Monotypic. Formerly found throughout New Zealand, this species became extinct as a breeding bird on South Island in the 1960s.

PODICEPS

The largest genus of grebes contains nine species. Four of these, Black-necked, Colombian, Silvery and Junín Flightless Grebes, are generally considered more closely related to each other than to the other five and have sometimes been placed in a separate genus, *Dytes*. The Great Grebe is also sometimes placed in a separate genus on its own, *Podicephorus*. Members of this genus occur worldwide.

GREAT GREBE *PODICEPS MAJOR*

Two subspecies have been described within the main range, which occupies the southern part of South America, though one is not accepted by all authorities. A small, isolated, population on the west coast further north has been proposed as a third subspecies.

RED-NECKED GREBE *PODICEPS GRISEGENA*

There are two subspecies, one in western Europe and western Asia, and the other on both sides of the northern Pacific, in eastern Asia and north-western North America. This is the only grebe of which the same subspecies occurs on both sides of the Pacific, having presumably evolved from a common ancestor.

GREAT CRESTED GREBE
PODICEPS CRISTATUS

This is the only grebe found in Europe, Asia, Africa and Australasia. Three subspecies have been described within this extensive range.

HORNED (OR SLAVONIAN) GREBE
PODICEPS AURITUS

Two subspecies occur, one in Eurasia, one in North America. The differences are very slight and some taxonomists consider it to be monotypic.

BLACK-NECKED GREBE
PODICEPS NIGRICOLLIS

Four isolated populations of this species exist: in Europe and south-west Asia, in eastern Asia, in southern Africa and in south-western North America. Only three subspecies have been named. This, and the next three species, are sometimes placed in a separate genus, *Dytes*.

COLOMBIAN GREBE *PODICEPS ANDINUS*

Monotypic, though sometimes considered as a subspecies of Black-necked Grebe. The bird was described for the first time only in 1945. It was extinct 30 years later, principally through loss of habitat.

SILVERY GREBE *PODICEPS OCCIPITALIS*

Two subspecies occur within the range of this species, which extends more or less the whole way down the western side of South America and also includes the southern tip.

JUNÍN FLIGHTLESS GREBE
PODICEPS TACZANOWSKII

Monotypic. Historically this flightless grebe was confined to a single lake in Peru, but it has recently been introduced to other, nearby, lakes as part of a programme to try and save it from extinction threatened by massive changes in the lake's ecosystem due to mining pollution.

HOODED GREBE *PODICEPS GALLARDOI*

Monotypic, though known to have hybridized with Silvery Grebe. This is the 'newest' grebe, discovered and described as a species as recently as 1974. It occurs in a very restricted range in southern South America.

AECHMOPHORUS

Two species, both occurring in North and Central America, make up this genus, though only since 1985, when taxonomists decided that what had previously been thought of as two colour phases of one species were in fact separate species. The main evidence came from breeding studies, which showed that birds of one colour selectively chose their own kind to breed, rather than taking a partner at random from the available mix of the two phases. The existing single species had two subspecies and this division has been maintained for both the separated species.

WESTERN GREBE
AECHMOPHORUS OCCIDENTALIS

Two subspecies are recognized, occurring respectively in the northern and southern parts of the range, which extends from southern Canada to Mexico.

CLARK'S GREBE *AECHMOPHORUS CLARKII*

There are two subspecies within what is currently taken to be the same range as that of the Western Grebe. The separation from the latter is so recent that any differences in the range of the two species have yet to be worked out in detail.

The preceding review shows that grebe populations are uneven in numbers and distribution around the world. Species can occur almost worldwide or be restricted to a single lake. Central and South America come out easily on top: 12 of the 22 species occur there, which points to the importance of this region as the evolutionary centre of the grebe family. Seven of these – Least, Pied-billed, White-tufted, Great, Silvery, Western and Clark's – have extensive ranges. The other five, however – Atitlán, Titicaca Flightless, Colombian, Junín Flightless and Hooded – have very restricted ranges, even down to a single lake. Three species, Red-necked, Horned and Black-necked, occur widely across the northern hemisphere in both Eurasia and North America. The Black-necked Grebe also occurs south of the equator, in southern Africa. The Little and Great Crested both occur in Eurasia and southern Africa, the former extending into Indonesia, the latter also found widely in Australia, and in New Zealand. Two species, Madagascar and Alaotra, are confined to the island of Madagascar, one with a very restricted range. The last group of grebes includes one species, the Australasian, which is widespread throughout Australasia (using that term in its widest sense to include Indonesia to the north and west and New Zealand to the east). A second, the Hoary-headed Grebe, occurs solely in Australia and New Zealand, and a third, the New Zealand Grebe, is confined to that country.

Size and Plumage

Grebes are very variable in size, but are easily recognizable by some very obvious characteristics, and combinations of characteristics, which are not found in other birds. The smallest of the family, the Least Grebe, measures no more than 21–22cm (8.5in) from bill tip to tail, and weighs on average as little as 116g (4oz). At the other end of the scale, the Great Grebe is up to 77cm (30in) long and may weigh 1.6kg (3.5lb), thus three and a half times longer and nearly 14 times heavier than the Least Grebe. (*See* Appendix I for size and weight of each species.) Grebes show very few plumage differences between the sexes, though in a few species the female is slightly paler or less patterned than the male, while the male's head plumes are generally a little brighter. In most species, males are on average larger than females and tend to have longer bills. These differences are not usually very well marked as there is always a considerable overlap in the measurements. Despite this, it is often possible to distinguish the male from the female of a pair by his slightly larger size. In this respect grebes are similar to geese, another group of birds where the sexes have identical plumage, but where the female almost invariably chooses a mate larger than herself.

Adult grebes have two principal plumages. In several species the more brightly coloured breeding dress includes a variety of contrastingly coloured and usually erectile plumes on the head. A duller non-breeding dress is worn for the rest of the year. Most species exhibit at least some chestnut or dark red colouring, usually on the neck. This varies from a small patch to almost the whole of the neck, sometimes extending on to the breast and along the flanks. Other species may have a very dark, often black, head and neck, or, conversely, have a pure, gleaming white neck and breast. The most conspicuous feature of many grebes in breeding plumage is their array of head plumes, taking the form of a ruff, often called a tippet (the name originally given to the capes made out of grebe feathers for ladies in the 19th century). Also noticeable are the crest and ear tufts (also known as auricular fans). Some species have just one of these features, while others have them all. These head adornments are often coloured chestnut or gold, usually in combination with very dark, or black, feathering to either side, or close by, to make them more conspicuous. The main purpose of this striking head plumage is in courtship display and aggressive behaviour. The feature is most developed in the genus *Podiceps*, reaching its most extravagant in the Great Crested Grebe. It is also present, though less marked, in the genera *Rollandia* and *Poliocephalus*. The *Aechmophorus* grebes have crests which they can both raise up and spread to the side, while those in the genus *Tachybaptus* have slightly elongated feathers on their head, which can be ruffled to give a round-headed appearance. The two *Podilymbus* species can also alter their head shape by raising their crown feathers.

The non-breeding plumage of grebes is always duller than when they are breeding. Most species moult into a plumage that is essentially dark or black above and white below. In migratory species, the post-breeding moult into non-breeding plumage often begins on the breeding grounds with the loss of the head plumes and continues through the migration, to be completed on arrival at the wintering grounds. At some stage, the wing feathers will be moulted simultaneously, rendering the bird flightless for three to four weeks. This can occur on the breeding grounds, as in some Great Crested Grebes, or more usually at one of the staging areas on migration, though birds that move only short distances may moult where they will be spending the winter. The total post-breeding moult takes at least two months and often up to three or even four. The gap between the end of this moult and the start of the moult back into breeding plumage is equally variable. In the case of the Great Crested Grebe there is hardly a pause at all, though in most species in the northern hemisphere one moult will be finished by October or November and the next one will not start until about March. The pre-breeding moult is generally accomplished in a shorter time, often only one to two months, and may not include the whole of the body, for example the feathers of the underparts may be kept for the full year.

The chicks of all the grebes except the two *Aechmophorus* species are characteristically striped dark and light from front to back on the head and continuing down the neck and often along the back. This striking pattern probably has advantages in giving the chicks some cryptic concealment from predators. The Western and Clark's Grebes lack this obvious striping, though a close examination shows that it is present, if only in shadowy outline. Instead, there is a grey crown to the otherwise whitish head and the body is darker above, paler below. Grebe chicks have three patches of bare skin on their head: one on the crown, which is slightly inflatable, and one on either side between the base of the bill and the eye. These probably have a thermo-regulatory function, allowing the chick to lose excess heat, but they also seem to have an important function as signals to the parents. They are normally very pale yellow in colour, but when the chick is hungry, or alarmed, they become flushed with blood, becoming a much more conspicuous bright red.

When the chicks moult out of their down and into their juvenile plumage, the striped pattern is retained around the head and neck, but the rest of the body becomes very like the non-breeding plumage of the adult. This plumage is kept through the first autumn and into the first winter. The young birds start to moult into their first summer plumage from about mid-winter onwards. By the spring they are very similar to the adult birds, but in the species that develop head plumes these will be smaller and less brightly coloured. Not until the second spring will full adult plumage be attained.

BEHAVIOUR

Great Crested Grebes were the subject of some of the pioneering studies of bird behaviour when first Edmund Selous and then Julian Huxley made observations on their courtship display in the first decade of the 19th century. Selous and Huxley described in detail the several different displays used in courtship and in aggressive encounters. They recognized the importance of the elaborate head plumes enhancing the birds' appearance in both courtship and threat; the collecting and carrying of weed during certain routines; and the fact that both sexes play equal roles. From their work, and later studies, came the vocabulary used to describe the different components of the displays: advertising, weed-ceremony, ghostly penguin dance, head-shaking, habit-preening,

11

bob-preening, water-dance, rushing, arch-clucking, and so on. Some of these are reasonably easy to understand from the name alone, others require explanation. This book is not the place for an exhaustive treatment of all the different displays of all the grebes, but descriptions of some of the principal displays will be found in the species accounts. In summary, the larger grebes, those in the *Podiceps* and *Aechmophorus* genera, have developed the most elaborate head adornments and the most elaborate displays to go with them. The mainly smaller species in the other four genera have less in the way of adornments and correspondingly simpler displays. However, these species tend to make much more use of their voice, uttering loud trills and often performing duets.

One category of display not described in any of the species accounts is that of platform behaviour. Grebes have to come out of the water to copulate, since they appear to lack the ability shown by wildfowl for the male to balance on top of the nearly submerged female for the brief duration of coition. Although a pair of grebes will copulate on a suitable flat area of shore or small islet, they usually build a special floating platform of water-weed for the purpose. This is almost identical to the nest, but is constructed well in advance of actual breeding, as pairing starts many weeks or even months beforehand. Having constructed the platform, one of the birds (not necessarily the female) will climb on to it, lie prone and call, sometimes also quivering its wings. The other bird will climb on to its back, copulate, then move forward over its head and back into the water again.

Most grebes are territorial, defending an area around the nest. In some cases the area is large enough to contain the food requirements of the adults and their young chicks, though in others they will move out of it to feed, especially as the young grow. Seven species – Hoary-headed, Black-necked, Silvery, Junín Flightless, Hooded, Western and Clark's – regularly nest in colonies, which in the more abundant species may be thousands strong, with the nests often only 1m (3ft 3in) apart. This gregariousness, as well as taking maximum advantage of

suitable nesting habitat and providing some protection against predators, is usually combined with feeding in dense flocks, often on concentrated food sources. Co-operative feeding may be used to enhance the likelihood of finding suitable prey.

Grebes as Divers

Grebes are supremely well adapted for diving, including the underwater pursuit and capture of prey. Their plumage is highly waterproof and very dense: each bird possesses a total of over 20,000 feathers. The legs are positioned right at the rear of the body, aiding both diving and swimming, above and below the water, while the three toes are broadly lobed as well as very slightly webbed. Grebes swim by pushing with both feet together. They do not use their wings underwater, instead keeping them closed tightly to their sides. Although the different species vary considerably in shape, with the length of neck, head and bill related to diving ability, they are all very well streamlined, with a slender head on a long neck, which ends in a comparatively narrow breast. Many diving birds use their long, stiff, tail feathers to aid underwater steering, but the tail of a grebe is reduced to nothing but a few, very short, soft feathers. The resulting rounded end to the body reduces drag through the water. Instead of steering with their tail, grebes use their legs, which have flexible joints providing good underwater manoeuvrability. The legs, which are also compressed from side to side to reduce water resistance, are comparatively large and heavy in relation to the rest of the body. This helps explain the shape of the larger species when swimming, with the rear end low in the water.

When a grebe dives, it does so either by leaping upwards and forwards, partially or even completely out of the water, or by simply pushing its head and neck downwards into the water and kicking with its legs. The initial jump allows the bird to enter the water at a greater angle and probably enables it to dive more deeply. Immediately before diving, the grebe will sleek down its feathers, squeezing out any air between them. It also expels the breath in its lungs. Mammals take in a breath before diving, but grebes and other diving birds exhale in order to reduce buoyancy. Grebes lack much of the interlinked mass of air sacs and hollows found in the bones of some waterbirds, for example wildfowl, which helps explain why they float much lower in the water than, say, ducks. The specific gravity of the grebe's body is thus closer to that of the water so they have to carry out less pre-diving preparation. Grebes can use this ability to adjust their position in the water, enabling them to stay almost completely submerged, with just the upper part of the head and bill showing above water, allowing them perfect concealment among water plants.

The length of time that any diving bird stays under water is governed by several factors such as the depth it reaches and/or the distance it travels before surfacing. Obviously, it is also affected by how quickly the bird captures its prey, which in turn depends on the availability of prey and the skill of the bird. Some birds will remain underwater to eat small prey, but come to the surface to deal with larger items. Different birds also adopt different strategies of making a few, prolonged dives with good recovery periods in between, or making lots of shorter dives more frequently. Most grebes feed in quite shallow water, so the length of their dives does not compare with that of some of the more accomplished species such as divers, auks and the seaducks. Many measurements have been taken of diving times among different species. However, without a lot of supplementary information that is often not available (in particular the depth of the water and what the birds are feeding on), these times are not always meaningful and certainly not comparable between different species or between different observations of the same species.

As a general rule, most of the larger grebes remain submerged for an average of 25–35 seconds, and the smaller ones for about half that. Extremes include the 85 seconds measured for a Great Crested Grebe in New Zealand – considerably longer than the maximum 56 seconds recorded during many studies of the same species in Europe. The difference is probably related to differences in habitat and prey availability in the two regions. Great Crested Grebes swimming underwater were found to average a speed of about 0.6m (2ft) per second, compared with a surface speed of about 0.28m (10in) per second. However, a grebe chasing a fish can easily achieve an underwater speed of about 2m (6ft 6in) per second and even, briefly, 3m per second (almost 10ft per second or nearly 7mph). Although most grebes feed in comparatively shallow water only a few metres deep, some of the larger species are capable of going down to perhaps 15m (50ft).

FOOD, FEEDING AND FEATHER EATING

Fish and aquatic invertebrates are the main foods of virtually all the grebes, though the proportions vary between species. Although, as a general rule, the longer-billed grebes take mainly fish and the longer the bill the larger the fish, there are a number of exceptions, not least the Black-necked Grebe's habit of feeding on brine shrimps. The smaller grebes concentrate more on invertebrates than on fish. For many species, diet will vary with the time of year, especially for migratory species whose winter and summer habitats differ. Thus Red-necked and Horned Grebes take a diversity of fish and invertebrate prey on their freshwater breeding lakes, but change to a much more exclusively fish diet in the winter, when they are mostly on the sea. The greater part of the diet of the Atitlán Grebe comprises freshwater crabs, which the bird can deal with because it has an exceptionally deep bill plentifully supplied with strong muscles. The diet of different grebes is discussed in several of the species accounts below.

A diving grebe may pursue its prey underwater, in the case of fish, or may simply pick aquatic invertebrates from the leaves of water plants. Other techniques

13

include swimming with the bill and eyes submerged, obviously searching for potential prey, some of which may be reached without diving or perhaps by just half submerging, almost upending. Surface feeding on invertebrates is quite common among some species while, in a few cases, the birds may catch flying insects in the air, even pursuing them over the water.

Birds deal with food in the stomach, which is divided into two sections: the proventriculus, where the digestive secretions are produced, and the ventriculus or gizzard, where the food is crushed by the strong, muscular walls. To aid this process, many birds ingest particles of grit, replenishing them from time to time. Only a few grebes do this, perhaps because, on the whole, their food is reasonably soft and easy to deal with, apart from the fish bones. Like birds of prey, grebes regurgitate indigestible parts such as bones, but have had to develop a unique way of coping with such dangerously sharp objects. While an owl's or a falcon's pellet consists of the bones safely contained within a mass of the fur or feathers of their prey, a fish has no such soft outer layer to perform the same function. Grebes, therefore, supply their own. They literally eat their own feathers in order to provide the required protective mass in which the fish bones can be safely enfolded. Adult grebes spend much time preening, during which they pluck out small breast and flank feathers and eat them, sometimes in quite large numbers. Not only that, but they feed their chicks with feathers too, from the moment they hatch, even before they have been given any other food.

There is some dispute about the exact purpose of feather eating. One suggestion is that the feathers wrap round the fish bones in the stomach and hold them there long enough for the stomach juices to digest them more fully, blunting the pointed ends, before they enter the intestines. However, it is extremely rare to find any bone fragments, or more than a few feathers, in the intestines of a grebe, so this theory has not received wide acceptance. Instead, the favoured explanation is that the feathers serve two purposes. Firstly, they are used to form the basis of pellets containing fish bones and the hard parts of invertebrates, permitting safe regurgitation. Secondly, dissected stomachs of grebes are very frequently found to contain a plug of feathers lodged in the exit to the gizzard, thus preventing any unwanted objects from getting into the thin-walled duodenum. The feathers themselves, once in the stomach, become partially digested, forming a greenish spongy material rather like felt – an ideal bone-wrapping medium. Confirmation of the pellet-forming theory comes from the knowledge that feather-eating is much more noticeable among the fish-eating grebes than those, like the Little Grebe, that eat more invertebrates. The Hoary-headed Grebe, which eats almost no fish at all, but lives on small aquatic arthropods, is believed not to eat feathers at all.

BREEDING

As will be apparent from the species accounts, grebes that breed in temperate regions have regular nesting seasons commencing in the spring and using territories adopted during the winter when pairs are formed. Those species breeding in the tropics tend to have prolonged seasons and will breed whenever conditions – water-level, weed growth and food supply – are suitable. This also applies to the grebes of Australia which react to the irregular rainfall of that country by breeding at any time of the year, often after lengthy movements to take advantage of newly flooded wetlands many hundreds of kilometres from their normal range.

Whilst a pair of grebes may have been indulging in courtship display for several months, breeding proper can be said to begin when the pair start to build their nest. Although they may already have built a number of platforms on which they will have been copulating, the nest is generally a more substantial structure, capable of lasting throughout the laying and incubation period. Sometimes the nest is built up on the base of an earlier platform, sometimes a completely fresh start is made, perhaps in a more sheltered situation. Nests are usually floating, anchored to surrounding water plants, but in shallow water the weed may sink until the nest rests on the bottom and the birds build it up from there. Both adults build the nest, bringing in available weed from the surrounding area, including stems, leaves and sometimes roots and small twigs, even, in some cases, bits of paper or other rubbish which the birds have found floating in the water. Although the larger grebes tend to build the largest nests, there is a lot of variation which may depend on factors such as water depth, availability of weed and conditions of shelter. Thus some nests can be 30–40cm (12–16in) high, with the bulk below water, and as much as 60cm (2ft) in diameter at the base, tapering to perhaps 30–45cm (12–18in) at the surface. A shallow cup, only 2–3cm (1in) deep, is formed in the centre of the nest and surrounded with loose pieces of weed, often finer than the rest of the nest. This will be used to cover the eggs if the incubating bird leaves.

The eggs of all the grebes are either chalky white in colour, or a very pale green or pale blue, generally fading to white within a few days. During the incubation period, the eggs usually become stained brown or red-brown, from contact with the always damp weed and with the feathers of the incubating birds which may become stained by salts in the water. Clutch size and other basic facts about the breeding biology of different species are summarized in Appendix II. The eggs are laid at intervals, usually of about 48 hours. Incubation starts with the first egg, either immediately it is laid or during the period before the second egg appears. Both parents incubate, taking it in turns which can vary very considerably in length, from as little as ten minutes to as much as eight hours overnight, when changeovers occur much less often than during the day, if at all. There is evidence from a few species that the female incubates in longer spells than the male and more usually incubates at night. There is also a tendency for the average length of spell to increase as incubation proceeds. Changeovers involve minimal ceremony,

perhaps a little greeting by head-shaking, but usually the incubating bird slips off into the water and its mate climbs straight on to the nest and settles on the eggs. If the incubating bird leaves the eggs before its mate is ready to take over – most usually when disturbed – then it covers the eggs with the surrounding weed, a very rapid operation accomplished with a couple of flicks of the head and bill. It then departs, having effectively concealed its eggs from passing predators and, perhaps more importantly, prevented them from chilling.

Hatching, like laying, takes place over a matter of days, though the hatching interval is often shorter than the two days between laying. The chicks are active more or less as soon as they have dried off. This they do both under the still-incubating bird and, especially in the larger species, by climbing on to the incubating parent's back and snuggling down among the wing feathers, which are slightly raised to accommodate them. During the few days that the whole clutch takes to hatch, the young stay on the nest or on the incubating adult, while the other parent brings food items of a suitable size for the chicks. Once all the young have hatched, the family leaves the nest. While one adult carries the brood on its back, the other catches prey and brings it to them, producing that most charming of sights, an adult feeding a chick as its head pokes out from among the wing feathers of the other parent. The length of time that the chicks are carried varies between species, being generally longer in the larger species. For example, Great Crested Grebe parents carry their young more or less all the time for about the first two weeks and may continue to do so, less regularly, for a further week beyond that. The young hardly ever go on to the water themselves during the first two weeks. It is almost as if they have an aversion to doing so, though it may be that their down is not very waterproof to start with. Switching from one parent to the other seems to be done as quickly as possible. The chicks do, however, sometimes get wet as it is not unknown for a parent to dive while still carrying the brood on its back. As the grebe's wings remain closed

15

during diving, the chicks should not be in any danger of being swept off.

Feeding of the chicks continues for some weeks after hatching, three or four in the Little Grebe and other small species, seven or eight in the Great Crested. In some grebes, the brood may be split between the parents part way through the rearing period and when this happens it is not unusual for each parent to favour one of the chicks in their care at the expense of the others, though the reason for this is unclear. Certainly the 'favourite' is fed first, so it may be a mechanism to ensure that at least one chick will be reared, if food becomes scarce, rather than allowing them all to starve. Several species of grebe consistently rear two or more broods, the second clutch often being laid well before the chicks of the first brood are independent, in which case they will be taken care of by one of the adults while the other one is incubating. The time when the chicks become fully independent is variable, even within the same species or within the same brood, but it usually coincides more or less with fledging. Some aggression can often be seen around this time, with the parents chasing the young away, though a favoured chick may be tolerated for a few weeks longer than the rest of the brood. Once independent, young grebes tend to form flocks which, in migratory species, often move separately from the adults, leaving them to spend some time moulting either before or during the migration. In sedentary species, the young gradually merge into winter flocks with the adults. In the species for which information is available, the birds breed for the first time when they are two years old.

CONSERVATION

Details of the status and conservation needs of each species, and some subspecies, are given in many of the species accounts, and summarized in Appendix III. The main sources of information are O'Donnel and Fjeldså (1997) and Rose and Scott (1997). The two publications include many of the same population totals, though there are some differences and some updated figures have been included in the Appendix. In summary, of the 22 species, two, the Atitlán Grebe of Guatemala and the Colombian Grebe, are believed to be extinct. The Alaotra Grebe of Madagascar very probably is, or if not then it is classified by the International Union for the Conservation of Nature as 'critically endangered' (facing an extremely high risk of extinction if the present circumstances do not change). Of the remaining 19 species and the 31 subspecies, the Junín Flightless Grebe is regarded as critically endangered and the race of the White-tufted Grebe that also occurs on Lake Junín is 'endangered' (facing a very high risk of extinction, but with perhaps a few more years left in which to attempt to save it). The Madagascar Grebe and the Titicaca Flightless Grebe are both classified as 'vulnerable' (facing a high risk of extinction and likely to be moved into the endangered category in the near future if the adverse factors affecting them remain unchanged). The same applies to no less than eleven different subspecies, made up of Australasian Grebe (six), Little Grebe (two), Great Crested Grebe (one), Western Grebe (one) and Clark's Grebe (one). The majority of the other species and subspecies are classified as being of 'least concern', meaning that there are no known threats to the global status, though there may be localized problems. However, one subspecies of White-tufted Grebe, four of Little Grebe, and one each of Great Crested and Black-necked Grebe are classified as 'data deficient' as there is not enough knowledge to be able to classify them with any certainty. These are, therefore, needing quite urgent survey work to be carried out so that they can be properly classified.

The sorry state of affairs outlined above and in Appendix III shows that six full species of grebe out of 22 in the world, and 11 subspecies out of 31, are classified as vulnerable or endangered, some of them critically so. This represents around one-third in each case. The relative abundance of some species shows that some grebes can be very successful in establishing themselves, but others have failed to do so, usually because they have become confined to very small areas or even single lakes, as in the case of the flightless species. Wetlands worldwide are a particularly threatened type of habitat, and often it is the shallowest waters – the ones often favoured by grebes – that are the most vulnerable to drainage, pollution and the introduction of alien fish species. Other factors may threaten larger lakes, including changes to the water level related to hydro-electric generation, which can be particularly damaging when the level is varied during the breeding season, either flooding nests or leaving them high and dry. Harvesting of reed from the lake shore, clearing of marshland vegetation to allow cattle grazing, and disturbance from fishing and pleasure boats have all had serious effects in different areas, sometimes on the same wetland, as have hunting and egg collecting. These are often regarded as necessary to the subsistence of local people, even though in some cases it seems to be carried on nowadays more as a tradition than as a necessity. It can also be very difficult to curtail, even if it is banned by law. Pollution from industrial and agricultural run-off can be a major problem, and a number of oil spills have killed grebes. Species that winter in shallow coastal waters are particularly at risk.

Despite this gloomy picture, some positive signs have emerged in recent years. There has been a growing awareness among conservation organizations and governments of the serious situation in which many grebes find themselves, especially as a result of man's activities. Coupled with this is a growing willingness to do something about it. Key grebe scientists such as Professor Storer and Dr Fjeldså have played a major part, firstly in finding out the status and distribution of some of the scarcer and more remote species and subspecies, and secondly in alerting the relevant organizations both nationally and worldwide. As a direct consequence of their work and that of others, many important wetland sites have been given protection under both local law and world conventions, such as the Ramsar Convention on Wetlands. However, while it may always be possible for birdwatchers and other lovers of wildlife in countries in Europe and North America to visit their local wetlands and marvel at the elaborate displays of the grebes breeding there, wetlands in the tropics and perhaps especially in South America and in parts of Africa and southern Asia will need much effort and resources to achieve the same. The development of green tourism has already had a beneficial, if modest, effect in some areas such as Madagascar, for example, where birdwatching tourists are eager to see some of the rarer birds. Such interest can only stimulate regional and national governments into realizing the value of the wildlife assets they ultimately control. Grebes form only part of this attraction, of course, but it is an important part, because their appeal is worldwide and because they are good markers of the health of wetlands. What better subject to use as a symbol of conservation than one of the oldest known groups of living birds?

THE SPECIES ACCOUNTS

Each of the 22 species accounts that follow begins with a brief statement on distribution, including all described races. Thereafter, rather than following a set content within each account, such as might be found in a scientific monograph on the group, with full descriptions of habitat, distribution, behaviour, breeding biology, voice and so on, the intention has been to convey information in a less scientific, less-structured format. The basic facts of size, weight, breeding biology, distribution and conservation status are tabulated in the first three appendices. Some of the species accounts may include a selection of these facts, but without any attempt at completeness. Instead, they look at features of particular relevance or interest which vary between species, sometimes concentrating on conservation threats, in other cases on displays, and in yet others on food and feeding habits, or status and distribution. In a few accounts, reference is made to the origin of the species' name, either English or Latin. Appendix IV details this information for all the species and subspecies. On the maps, green indicates presence all the year round, yellow in the breeding season only, and hatched green where occurrence is irregular.

17

LITTLE GREBE

TACHYBAPTUS RUFICOLLIS

— PALEARCTIC RACE *T.r.ruficollis*: Europe and western Russia, North Africa.
— IRAQI RACE *T.r.iraquensis*: South-eastern Iraq and south-western Iran.
— AFRICAN RACE *T.r.capensis*: Africa south of the Sahara, including Madagascar; also Indian sub-continent including Sri Lanka east to Burma.
— ASIAN RACE *T.r.poggei*: South-east Asia, north through China, Korea, Taiwan and Japan to Kuriles.
— PHILIPPINE RACE *T.r.philippensis*: Northern Philippines.
— MINDANAO RACE *T.r.cotabato*: Mindanao.
— CENTRAL INDONESIAN RACE *T.r.tricolor*: Islands from Sulawesi to Timor and New Guinea.
— SOUTHERN INDONESIAN RACE *T.r.vulcanorum*: Islands from Java to Timor.
— NEW GUINEA RACE *T.r.collaris*: Eastern Papua New Guinea, New Britain, New Ireland and Solomons.

THE TAXONOMY OF THIS SPECIES IS BY NO MEANS straightforward and could well be subject to future change. Of the nine subspecies listed above, the five occurring in the Philippines, Indonesia and New Guinea are the least known in terms of distribution and habits. Intergrades, for example between *philippensis* and *cotabato* and between *tricolor* and *collaris* have been reported and it may be that neither pair justifies separate subspecific status. On the other hand, the birds of Java have been described as a separate race, as have those on the Ryukyu islands, between Taiwan and Japan. The main factors used in separating the different races have been size, general coloration and the amount of white on the secondaries. The iris colour varies strikingly, being red-brown in the Palearctic and African races, and yellow in the Asian.

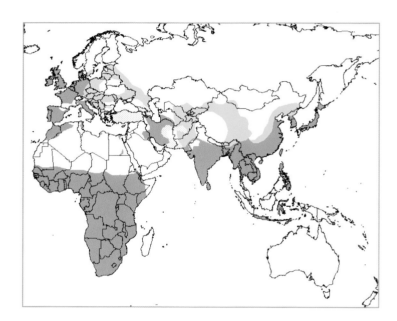

The Little Grebe is a noisy bird. Its high-pitched, whinnying trills ring out across the water as the birds court each other or drive away rivals. Although courtship occurs in two main periods, during September and October and again in February and March, it can be observed, and heard, in almost every other month, too. The most frequent courtship behaviour in the late summer is known as the hunched-display, when one bird swims towards another with its body plumage fluffed up and its wings slightly raised. The neck is tucked in and the bill pointing down, perhaps to emphasize that no threat is intended but that this is a friendly, but suitably tentative, approach. Some care is needed here because

the hunched-display can also be used as a preliminary to an attack. As the birds get close to each other, one utters a long trill, perhaps lasting three or four seconds. In the initial stages of courtship, the other bird may ignore this, or may respond. As the pair bond becomes stronger, so both birds will indulge in mutual displays involving them both adopting the hunched position and both trilling. Two closely related displays take place, involving both birds of a well-mated pair. The first is the triumph-display which takes place following the successful driving away of a rival or an intruder. The second is a more subdued version, the trilling-display.

An aggressive encounter may start at the boundary of two territories. The opposing Little Grebes hold their

necks up straight, with feathers raised on the head, and tails cocked. They utter prolonged trills, a harsher-sounding, slightly lower-pitched trill than that used in courtship. Birds have been observed trilling at each other on the boundaries of conjoining territories for as much as five minutes with hardly a break in the sound. However, if the situation deteriorates into actual attack, then the head and neck are lowered, bill pointing at the opponent, and legs and feet vigorously splashing in the water, kicking up a spray. Finally, the feet are dug in properly, propelling the bird rapidly over the surface, pattering or even skidding along as it heads towards its rival. There may be actual contact, or at the last minute the attacking bird dives and comes up underneath the other bird, pecking it. Depending on the reaction of the bird being attacked, the fight may develop in one of two ways. If the bird being attacked turns to flee, then it may grow into an out-and-out physical assault during which the aggressor throws itself on top of the escaping bird, pecks at its head and neck and tries to force it under water. If, however, the opponent does not turn away and attempt to leave the scene, the two birds will slug it out breast to breast, pushing against each other, bodies raised up out of the water, bills stabbing at each other and, for good measure, kicking with the feet as well. The vigour of such encounters is remarkable.

Eventually, the aggressive encounter comes to an end, one bird the victor, the other vanquished. The latter adopts an appeasing posture, often prone on the water, the bill submerged, removed from sight as an offensive weapon before the bird swims away, feathers sleeked down, trying to appear as non-threatening as possible. The victor then returns to its mate and they both go into their triumph-ceremony, hunching themselves in the water, coming face to face and then trilling in a prolonged duet, their rippling calls sounding together. They may then move into their trilling-ceremony, which can last for many minutes, the birds swimming close together, turning their heads from side to side. Pairs of Little Grebes also indulge in diving together often pattering

over the water for a few metres beforehand. As with many other grebes, they may surface carrying pieces of weed and drop them in front of each other in a kind of simulated nest-building. Displays can continue out of the water on the nest platform, which is built well before laying takes place.

Although there is some movement to winter quarters, where the birds may gather in loose flocks, many Little Grebes remain in pairs on their territory summer and winter, defending them against intruders. It is probable, therefore, that the pair bond lasts the life of the birds. The breeding season starts early in western Europe. The first eggs appear in late February and, with second, or rarely third, broods, the last young may be hatching in late August or early September. The four to six eggs are laid in the shallow cup of the nest platform, which floats on the water, attached to waterweeds and usually placed in emergent vegetation so that it is well concealed. The young chicks are carried on their parents' backs under the wings, but less frequently than in some other species. Instead, they are brought back to the nest, or the parents build extra platforms within the territory and look after them there, brooding them in rain and at night. When the young are small, their parents dive for food and then feed them bill to bill. As they grow, however, the prey may be released just in front of the chick, teaching it to catch food for itself. The main foods are aquatic invertebrates of many kinds, especially larvae, and small fish. There is some evidence that fish are a more important part of the diet in Africa.

Information on the number of Little Grebes is distinctly patchy. Quite good counts have been carried out in some western European countries, but as one goes further east and south, so the counts become estimates and some of the estimates become guesses. There are believed to be about 80,000 breeding pairs in Western Europe, with nearly three-quarters of those in Britain, Ireland, Germany, Spain, Portugal and, especially, the eastern European countries of Hungary, Poland, Croatia, Romania, Ukraine and the Czech Republic. The

20

populations in most of these countries are regarded as stable or showing some decline, mainly through loss of habitat. One complicating factor is that the species is vulnerable to freezing conditions, so numbers may fluctuate considerably, with sharp drops following severe winters.

The Iraqi subspecies *iraquensis* is thought to be very few in number. The main range lies in the marshes at the confluence of the Tigris and Euphrates rivers and this area has undergone massive drainage in the last 10–20 years. A figure of 6,000 was estimated in 1997, but it could be much less. There are probably under 100,000 of the African subspecies *capensis* actually in Africa and perhaps the same number, or more, in the Indian subcontinent part of the range. The Asian race *poggei* may well be as numerous as *capensis*, though that is largely guesswork. The numbers of the various races in Indonesia east to Papua New Guinea are completely unknown. It is quite probable that some of the island subspecies, e.g. *cotabato*, could be numbered in the very low thousands or even hundreds, though this will not necessarily mean that they are endangered unless their habitat is under threat. Unfortunately, this seems only too likely, as drainage of wetlands for agriculture is one of the biggest problems faced by all waterbirds worldwide.

On the plus side, the Little Grebe has shown itself to be very adaptable by quickly colonizing new wetlands, even though these may be no bigger than farm ponds and small reservoirs. Provided there is an adequate growth of aquatic vegetation and consequent populations of invertebrates and small fish, the birds will find such sites suitable. One paradoxical benefit to the Little Grebe has come with the introduction of fish to freshwater wetlands in Madagascar. As the two species accounts show, the Alaotra Grebe and the Madagascar Grebe have both retreated, the former to extinction in the face of various threats, one of which is the Little Grebe, which is enjoying more success because its diet in that part of the world is more dependent on fish than invertebrates.

21

Australasian Grebe

Tachybaptus novaehollandiae

— AUSTRALIAN RACE *T.n.novaehollandiae*: Australia, including Tasmania, New Zealand and southern New Guinea.
— VANUATU RACE *T.n.leucosternos*: Vanuatu and New Caledonia.
— RENNELL ISLAND RACE *T.n.rennellianus*: Rennell Island, Solomon Islands group.
— JAVA RACE *T.n.javanicus*: Java, Indonesia.
— TIMOR RACE *T.n.timorensis*: Timor, Indonesia.
— SANGIHE-TALAUD RACE *T.n.fumosus*: Sangihe and Talaud Islands, Sulawesi, Indonesia.
— NEW GUINEA RACE *T.n.incola*: Northern New Guinea.

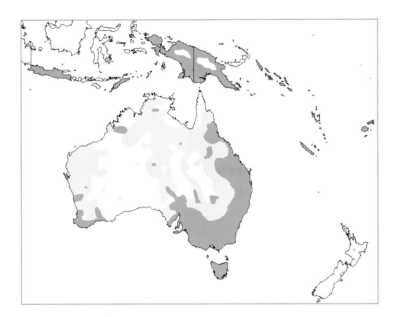

THE TAXONOMY OF THIS GREBE IS STILL SOMEWHAT tentative as it was only separated from the Little Grebe, of which it used to be regarded as a subspecies, in the early 1940s. It was the presence of two apparent subspecies in New Guinea, living side by side but not interbreeding, that stimulated the decision to split them. Not all the island races are sufficiently well known for their current subspecific status to be certain, though their geographical separation is a good pointer. The differences between them rely mainly on slight variations in size and overall colouring.

The similarity between this species and Little Grebe is readily apparent. Both have the patch of bare skin around the gape at the base of the bill, the same combination of black and chestnut on the head and neck, and overall similar body coloration. However, the differences are quite obvious, too, especially the much reduced area of chestnut on the Australasian Grebe's neck, present only on either side of the upper neck and reaching up to behind the eye, while the gape patch is yellower and the iris more yellow-orange than red. The Australasian Grebe is on average a little smaller but this is hardly a good field characteristic.

Not surprisingly the various races scattered throughout New Guinea and Indonesia have been very little studied and almost nothing is known about their numbers or current status, though it is perhaps safe to assume that all are potentially at risk from the decline in their wetland habitat. For one race though, *fumosus*, occurring on the

Sangihe-Talaud islands off the north coast of Sulawesi, there is another type of threat altogether. It was stated in the early 1990s that this race may be confined to the crater lake of a large volcano, Gunung Awu, on just one island, Great Sangihe. This information has been repeated since, but one wonders how up-to-date it is, because the volcano is reported to have erupted violently in 1966, for the first time since 1931, completely ejecting its crater lake, which was about 1km (620yd) across. The lake apparently reformed, but was then largely drained by a smaller eruption in 1992. There are a great many islands in the group, not all of them inhabited, so clearly surveying them for the grebe would be a difficult job, and it is possible that the grebe still survives on some of them.

Chris Rose

Surveys of Vanuatu suggest that the race there, *leucosternos*, is more widespread than previously thought and may number a few thousand individuals. It seems unlikely that any of the other four races, *rennellianus*, *javanicus*, *timorensis* and *incola*, have populations any larger than this and they could be a lot smaller, but there is a serious lack of information and an urgent need to survey the areas, identify their ranges and major haunts (if any), and see what problems these birds are facing. However, in a time of threats to so many birds, it is a great deal harder to attract funds for looking after subspecies than for trying to save full species.

If the island races of the Australasian Grebe may be cause for concern, at least the nominate subspecies in Australia is numerous and believed to be stable overall, though there may be local declines. The bird is widespread throughout all the areas with permanent wetlands and is capable of expanding into areas with temporary wetlands after periods of extensive rains. Thus it inhabits the whole of eastern and south-eastern Australia, as well as the south-west, and expands out of these areas over considerable distances when conditions allow. The first record on Tasmania was not until 1964, but breeding was reported the following year and there has been a scattering of records each year since, though whether the population, put at about 50 birds, is self-sustaining or is being reinforced from mainland Australia is not known. Within Australia there are estimated to be about 500,000, a figure based on partial surveys together with estimates calculated on the basis of available, permanent, wetlands. In the event of successive rainy seasons with increased breeding potential, then the population would probably rise, at least temporarily, above this.

A more extraordinary colonization was that of New Zealand, which took place even more recently. A single bird turned up in Otago, South Island, in April 1968 and stayed until January 1969. Then in August 1972 a pair appeared in Auckland, North Island, and stayed for several weeks, during which they displayed a little. Other birds turned up in the next year or two and soon pairs were breeding on both islands. Numbers have remained small, however – probably fewer than 50 individuals – and it is not yet certain that the species will become a permanent resident. The appearance of birds on both islands over a few years suggests some kind of vagrancy rather than a single influx. Australasian Grebes are probably not migrants in the true sense of the word, making regular seasonal movements. However, some birds breeding in Queensland, in the north of the range, are suspected of migratory behaviour, and others further south may move from breeding areas inland to more coastal wetlands, though not actually appearing on tidal waters. Instead, they respond to periods of drought and rains, staying put during the former, but capable of rapid exploitation of temporary wetlands and able to move hundreds of kilometres for the purpose. This ability is shared with many other waterbirds in the country and has clearly evolved to enable the birds to take advantage of the erratic, but often very extensive, increase in availability of wetlands for breeding. On occasions, the movement takes place so quickly that the necessary invertebrate food has yet to build up in the new waters, so the grebes may gather in hundreds on the nearest permanent water before eventually dispersing to breed.

Almost any freshwater wetland is acceptable to the Australasian Grebe, provided it has an adequate food supply and some aquatic vegetation in which, and from which, to construct a nest. Losses of wetland habitat through drainage and agricultural changes, and in some areas increased salinity following water extraction, have, in some cases, led to local declines in numbers. However, these declines have often been offset by the creation of numerous small farm reservoirs and ponds, which have proved ideal for the birds. The main breeding season is from September to December, but opportunistic breeding will take place outside this period and includes August and the months from January to April. In good conditions, two or even three broods are possible. The second clutch is laid when the first brood of young are about three weeks old and beginning to fend for

themselves, catching their own food and not being fed by the parents, though they will not fledge for a further three or four weeks. The young of the first brood may help rear those of the second brood, something which appears not to have been reported for the Little Grebe.

Not surprisingly, given the close relationship between the Australasian Grebe and the Little Grebe, the courtship and territorial displays are very similar. The Australasian Grebe, while holding territories, often throughout the year, is not quite so aggressive towards intruders as the Little Grebe. Indeed, while a small pond or reservoir will only be able to accommodate a single pair which will quickly drive others away, on larger waters, with dense stands of reeds, the birds may nest in loose colonies. There are also records of large clutches where two females are thought to have laid in the same nest. The birds accompany their displays with loud trills, just like Little Grebes, though the trills of Australasian Grebes have been described as less strong and also slightly shorter.

Within Australia itself, the Australasian Grebe is obviously secure and not threatened as a population. Elsewhere, though, there is considerable cause for concern about the other subspecies, as there has to be for any small population of birds confined to a handful of islands. Vital though it is to improve our knowledge, the difficulty of carrying out even basic surveys means it is difficult to know what, if anything, can be done.

MADAGASCAR GREBE
TACHYBAPTUS PELZELNII

— Occurs throughout Madagascar.

THE LATEST (1997) ESTIMATE OF THE NUMBERS OF Madagascar Grebes suggests that there are between 5,000 and 10,000, but there has certainly been a substantial decline in the last 40 years. If, as seems probable, it is still continuing, then the lower figure may be closer to the actual total. The fact that the grebe is reasonably widespread in Madagascar, though nowhere numerous, makes estimating its population quite difficult. While there is general agreement that there are fewer now than there were 40 years ago, there are no actual figures from that period.

The Madagascar Grebe occurs on a wide variety of freshwaters, large and small, permanent and temporary, still and (occasionally) running, and from near sea-level to about 2,000m (6,500ft). One common requirement is an abundance of aquatic vegetation which provides shelter for its main foods: small fish and freshwater invertebrates. The principal reasons for the decline in population appear to be closely linked to the decline in the numbers and extent of wetlands in the country as well as to a decline in water quality at some of those that remain. Right across Madagascar, wetlands and their associated marshes have been drained and converted into rice fields. In some areas, agricultural and other run-offs have caused serious pollution.

Those wetlands which have been less drastically altered in a physical sense include many where non-native fish have been introduced in order to boost local fishing. Two different types of fish have been brought in, both equally damaging to the grebes. Tilapia are a fast-growing group of fish native to mainland Africa which have proved ideal for aquaculture. They are largely vegetarian so have also been used to reduce waterweed problems in reservoirs. In some of the wetlands of Madagascar they have had a devastating effect on the aquatic vegetation, especially the large areas of water lily which often provide the main feeding areas for the Madagascar Grebe. The second introduced fish is black bass. This predator takes other smaller fish and also the chicks of grebes and other waterbirds.

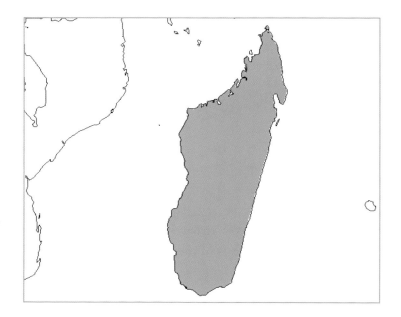

As the Madagascar Grebe gets scarcer so it becomes more vulnerable to habitat changes. It also becomes potentially more vulnerable to competition. The Little Grebe occurs in Madagascar, having apparently spread there naturally from Africa in the last 100 years. The account of the Alaotra Grebe reveals the effect that the Little Grebe had on that species by hybridizing it into extinction. The Little Grebe can also hybridize with the Madagascar Grebe, but so far examples are quite rare. However, as it becomes more numerous and the Madagascar Grebe becomes scarcer, so the potential for interbreeding can only increase. And the reason the Little Grebe is likely to continue to increase in numbers takes us back to the introduced fish. The effect of the Tilapia in reducing the amount of aquatic vegetation has been shown to reduce the freshwater invertebrate population more than the fish population of the wetlands. The almost wholly fish-eating Little Grebe therefore has not suffered from the reduction in invertebrates, whereas the Madagascar Grebe certainly has.

Madagascar is an island of great biological riches. Measuring about 1,600km (1,000 miles) long by about 600km (370 miles) at its widest point, the island has just

Chris Rose

under twice the land surface area of Britain and Ireland combined. That area holds an astonishing total of 106 endemic breeding birds, including three endemic families and no less than 32 endemic genera. There are also more than 50 endemic mammals, over 200 endemic reptiles, 148 different species of endemic frog and over 6,000 species of endemic plants. One species of grebe, the Alaotra, has almost certainly already become extinct, while the Madagascar Grebe must be regarded as vulnerable and perhaps even endangered. There is a great deal of interest in Madagascar's unique fauna and flora, reflected in the various research programmes and in the funding for conservation that comes from international agencies. Wildlife tourism is also very important and is increasing as tour firms bring groups eager to see some of the unique species. To what extent this can take its place alongside the undoubted need to maximize Madagascar's economy is one of the more difficult judgements for the government to make, but the survival of some of these species, which perhaps include the Madagascar Grebe, hangs on the right decisions being taken.

Rather little is known about the breeding habits or displays of the Madagascar Grebe. The main breeding season appears to be the period from February to April, after the rainy season has filled the permanent wetlands and created temporary ones. However, there appears to be a second breeding period, in the spring, from about August to October. Nests have been found both scattered as if in territories and close together in small colonies. No birds have ever been recorded off the island, but there are movements within it, especially after the end of the breeding season, when small flocks, once as many as 150, may gather on larger lakes.

28

ALAOTRA GREBE

TACHYBAPTUS RUFOLAVATUS

— Confined to Lake Alaotra and a few other wetlands in north-central Madagascar.
Endangered or, more probably, extinct.

THIS SMALL, BLACK-CAPPED GREBE WITH A CINNAMON chin and neck is also known as the Rusty Grebe, and as Delacour's Grebe after the distinguished French ornithologist who first described it as a separate species in 1932. Sadly, it is almost certainly extinct, not having been positively identified since about 1985. Although it has been suggested that as many as 20 pairs survived into the 1990s, there is very limited evidence for this optimism. This is because, although it has certainly declined in numbers because of habitat deterioration and over-hunting, the coup de grace has been delivered by another species, the Little Grebe, with which it has hybridized to the point where it is extremely doubtful that any pure-bred Alaotra Grebes remain.

The hybridization with the Little Grebe is not a new phenomenon, although it certainly accelerated in recent years. It was already happening in the 1920s and 1930s, when the first birds were collected at Lake Alaotra. The lake, the largest in Madagascar, lies in the northern half of the island about 100km (62 miles) from the east coast and at an altitude of about 1,000m (3,300ft) in the Central Highlands plateau. It is quite shallow and extends over some 220sq km (85sq miles) of open water while there is a further 350sq km (135sq miles) of adjacent marshland. In recent decades it has been subject to considerable man-made changes which, cumulatively, have drastically altered the ecosystem to the detriment of not just the grebe but much of the other wildlife, too.

The three main changes, which have taken place over the last 100 years, but at an increasing rate in the last 50, have been the introduction of exotic fish, the removal of large areas of marsh vegetation, and the deforestation of the surrounding hills. Two different types of fish have been introduced: firstly carp and other plant-eaters, which have destroyed large areas of water-lilies, for example, thus removing vital cover for invertebrates and native fish; and secondly predatory fish, which have

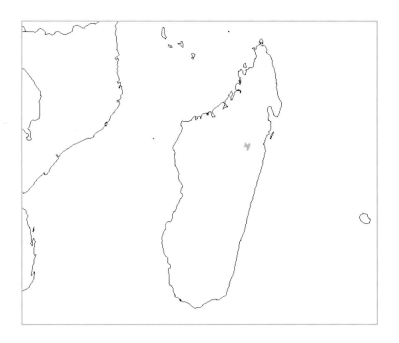

further reduced the natural food of the grebes and, perhaps, also eaten their young. The subsequent fishing industry has adopted monofilament nets which are undoubtedly killing many different kinds of diving birds. The Alaotra area of Madagascar has become a very important rice-growing region and this has led to the removal of some of the extensive stands of papyrus and reeds which formerly surrounded the lake. Other problems include the run-off of pesticides and fertilizers into the water, and the silting of the lake due to deforestation of the hills and consequent soil erosion.

If these changes directly affected the Alaotra Grebe, one of them had an unexpected indirect effect. The introduction of herbivorous fish, including Tilapia, from 1945 onwards, attracted Little Grebes to the lake in much increased numbers and the hybridization that was already taking place increased. When the first specimens were collected in 1929, Jean Delacour described two slightly different plumages which he thought were probably colour phases, with differences in the colouring of the face, throat and upper neck. In fact what he

was seeing were signs of hybridization with Little Grebes, as is made clear by the description of the type specimen in his 1933 paper on the grebes of Madagascar. The increase in numbers of Little Grebes has meant that few if any birds thought to be pure Alaotra Grebes were found during the surveys undertaken in the 1970s and 1980s. The last grebes to be seen were 12 in December 1982 and two, together with some very obvious hybrids, in September 1985. Surveys in during the 1989–1990 breeding season failed to find any that could be called Alaotra Grebes.

During the last 20 years, small numbers of grebes were found not just on other waters close by Lake Alaotra, but much further afield, as at Antsalova on the west coast and Isalo, well to the south. These discoveries were initially interpreted as a much-needed range expansion, but if so it was one forced on the birds by the deterioration at Lake Alaotra and none has resulted in colonization by pure-bred birds. Indeed, as the Alaotra Grebe is much shorter-winged than the Little Grebe, verging on the point of flightlessness, it seems reasonable to interpret the fact that some birds had managed to move several hundred kilometres to Antsalova and Isalo as proof that they were, in fact, hybrids.

Little or nothing is known about the displays of the Alaotra Grebe, though it can be assumed that they must have been very similar to those of the Little Grebe, in order for hybridization to have taken place. Breeding was occurring in the period April to June when it was first described, but in 1960 there were active nests between January and March. The diet has been assumed to be almost entirely fish.

It appears that another example of Madagascar's unique bird life has disappeared. Sadly, the Alaotra Grebe is not the only endemic to have been lost at the one site. Lake Alaotra was also the main haunt of the Madagascar Pochard, which has not reliably been seen since 1991.

LEAST GREBE

TACHYBAPTUS DOMINICUS

— CARIBBEAN RACE *T.d.dominicus*: Northern Caribbean, including Bahamas, Greater Antilles and Virgin Islands.
— CENTRAL AMERICAN RACE *T.d.brachypterus*: Southern Texas, Mexico to Panama.
— BAJA CALIFORNIAN RACE *T.d.bangsi*: Southern Baja California, Mexico.
— SOUTH AMERICAN RACE *T.d.speciosus*: South America, south to northern Argentina and southern Brazil.
— A FIFTH RACE, *T.d.eisenmanni*, living in the lowlands of western Ecuador, is recognized by some authorities.
— Races separated mainly on size.

THE LEAST GREBE LIVES UP TO, OR PERHAPS THAT SHOULD be down to, its name as the smallest of the grebe family. It is much the tiniest grebe in the Americas, and slightly smaller than the Little Grebe of Eurasia, Africa and Australasia. The differences between the races are mainly to do with size and colouring. The smallest race is *bangsi*, which is also paler than the others. The largest is *dominicus*. Little is known about the status of the different subspecies, except that they are all thought to number only a few thousands, with the exception of *speciosus*, which might number 20,000–30,000, if only because of the sheer size of its range. There is no detailed information on trends in numbers of any of the races. The species throughout its extensive range shows considerable adaptability to different types of wetland, which is likely to enable it to maintain its overall numbers, though one or more of the subspecies, with their much more limited range, could be threatened by changing conditions.

All the subspecies are described as sedentary, though some of those in South America, especially in the south of the range in Argentina, may be migratory. Local dispersals take place especially to take advantage of temporary wetlands appearing after the rainy season. The birds leave when these dry out. Newly created wetlands, such as farm reservoirs and ponds, are quickly colonized, suggesting that the birds are on the move quite a lot, if only locally. Their choice of habitat is certainly wide, varying from ponds and even large roadside ditches to large lakes, and also including slow-flowing rivers and streams, marshes, and mangrove swamps. The only constant factor among all these different wetlands is ample vegetation, even to the extent of being almost completely overgrown, as in marshland where there may be only a few small patches of open water.

Least Grebes use the ample vegetation of their chosen wetlands not only for building and anchoring their nests. It also harbours their main food of aquatic invertebrates, especially the adults and larvae of water beetles, water bugs, spiders, and dragonflies. As well as these, the birds also take tadpoles, small fish and crustaceans such as shrimps and small crabs. Much of their food is obtained by diving, often preceded by swimming along with bill and eyes submerged, searching for prey. These grebes also feed on the surface, pecking food items off the water or even chasing flying insects, like dragonflies, and catching them in the air. Ants are included in the diet, too,

presumably picked off low branches touching the water. Least Grebes are often seen feeding in company with other birds, including dabbling ducks, coot and other grebes. They may gain some benefit from picking up insects disturbed by these larger birds.

The displays and calls of the Least Grebe have been described by the noted grebe expert Professor Robert Storer. The advertising call, given when a pair is separated, has been likened to a high-pitched sound like 'gamp', uttered once or twice a second. When uttering it, the bird stretches its neck, lifts its head up, sleeks down the feathers of its body and raises itself out of the water so that the white underparts show at the front. Although it is used when a bird is alarmed, its main purpose seems to be to reinforce the pair bond. The other principal sound is a trill, given frequently during courtship, often by the pair trilling together with alternating notes. There seem to be several stimuli for trilling. It occurs after the successful conclusion of an aggressive encounter with another grebe, or when the birds come together at the nest, or even in response to the trilling of a neighbouring pair of grebes.

Least Grebes are territorial breeders and will defend a territory around the nest, if a comparatively small one of perhaps 500–1,400sq m (5,300–15,000sq ft). There are frequent chases, such as when a territorial male vigorously sees off neighbouring males, using its wings and feet in skittering semi-flight across the water. On one occasion a male, apparently defending his mate, pursued another male, which was skittering in zig-zags, by diving and following its progress under water before surfacing close to it. Males will sometimes fight, pushing at each other breast to breast and attempting to strike each other with their feet. One male Least Grebe successfully defended an area with a radius of about 12m (40ft) around its nest from a pair of the much larger Pied-billed Grebes.

The breeding season is very extended. Nests have been found in Texas in every month of the year, with eggs being found even in January and December. Most nesting takes place between April and August, however. In the tropics, there is a tendency to breed during the rainy season and for pairs in any one area to breed more or less at the same time. One pair, studied in Cuba, began breeding in July and were still at it the following May. They laid five successive clutches of eggs in the six months between July and January, rearing young each time. They then laid a sixth clutch in late February, which failed, followed by a seventh, which hatched in late April. They built an eighth nest in May, but hatched no young from it. In total, they laid 35 eggs in the eight clutches, hatched 27 of them and reared no less than 23 chicks – a phenomenal effort. In between taking his turn at incubation, the male was seen to provide food for the young of two older broods. At the same time both parents were feeding one three-week-old brood while incubating the next clutch. There have not been enough detailed studies to show whether this was a unique happening. Could it even be typical, on waters with an obvious abundance of food, for these grebes not only to rear large numbers of young but also to have the energy which the female would have needed to produce eight successive clutches? Although five out of 17 clutches recorded in Texas failed because of predation or infertility, more than 90 per cent of the young that did hatch were successfully reared.

Least Grebes are at risk from a number of predators. A pair of Bat Falcons was observed in El Salvador to kill several Least Grebes, striking them as they swam on the water, dragging them over the surface to a convenient perch and then skinning them and eating just the breast muscles. Turtles have been reported as predators of the young grebes, as have larger species of fish, which the grebes perhaps avoid by preferring small, and temporary, waters for breeding. Despite these natural hazards, Least Grebes are apparently holding their own throughout their range without too many problems. However, there is a need to monitor both them and their habitat to make certain this is the case.

Pied-billed Grebe

Podilymbus podiceps

— NORTH AMERICAN RACE *P.p.podiceps*: Central Canada and United States, Mexico south to Panama.
— SOUTH AMERICAN RACE *P.p.antarcticus*: South America from Panama south to southern Chile and southern Argentina.
— ANTILLEAN RACE *P.p.antillarum*: Greater and Lesser Antilles.
— The three races are very similar in appearance, varying slightly in size.

ALTHOUGH 15 SPECIES OF GREBE OCCUR IN THE AMERICAS, the Pied-billed Grebe is the only one that breeds widely in both North and South America. It occupies shallow freshwaters with an abundance of aquatic vegetation growing both in the water and around the shores. In the north of its range in North America, the Pied-billed Grebe is a true migrant, moving north to breed widely in southern Canada and also throughout much of Saskatchewan and Alberta to the extreme south of Northern Territories. The Canadian part of the range is vacated in winter, as is much of the central United States. These birds move south and west to winter in the southern United States from California to Florida and Mexico where they merge with the mostly sedentary populations in those regions. Southward migration can be seen from as early as August, as small ponds dry out, and continues throughout September to November. Some birds are still moving south in December, especially if cold weather sets in. Northward-moving birds can be seen from February onwards with the peak in April. Almost all the migration occurs at night, and the birds seek a suitable area of water to rest on as dawn approaches. Returns from ringed birds show movements of up to 2,280km (1,415 miles), with an indication of north-south migration as birds follow the main flyways down the east and west coasts and the central Mississippi-Missouri valley.

The migratory habit, especially on the east coast of North America (where the birds breed as far north as southern Quebec, New Brunswick and Nova Scotia and then migrate south into Virginia, the Carolinas and Florida) has led to a scattering of records on the other side of the Atlantic. The first such record was in October 1927, when an immature female was collected on the

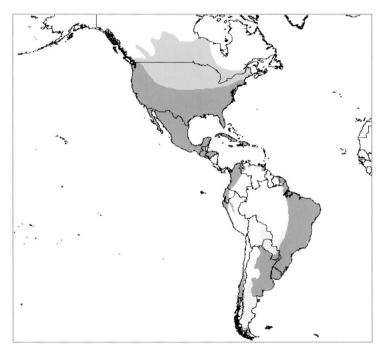

Azores. There was then a considerable gap before the next occurrence, also on the Azores, in October 1954, then a shorter interval before the third record, of a bird on a reservoir in south-west England in December 1963, quickly followed by the fourth, on the Azores again, in October 1964. This last bird was captured alive, and although it is not reported how, as it died the next day, it may well have been injured or exhausted. In June 1965, one appeared on a reservoir in northern England and stayed right through until November. In August of the same year, another bird was found on a reservoir in south-west England only a few kilometres from the location of the 1963 record. This one stayed until late October. What has been supposed to be the same bird reappeared on the same reservoir between May and November 1966, May and October 1967 and May and July 1968. It was also seen in 1968 on the original

neighbouring water. Its presence for four consecutive summers set a pattern which was followed by other long-staying returning individuals in later years. What has never been discovered is where the original regular visitor spent the rest of each year, though given the coastal wintering habit of the birds in North America, it could have found a sheltered south coast harbour or lagoon and been overlooked there among a mass of other wintering waterbirds.

There were seven records on the European side of the Atlantic in the 1960s, dropping to four in the 1970s, but including the first record in Iceland. In the 1980s and 1990s, there were 11 and 22 records respectively, with the majority (18) in Britain, but also some in Ireland (5), the Azores (4), France (3), the Netherlands (2) and the Canary Islands (1). Several of these stayed for many months or have returned in successive years. One was a male which turned up on a small reservoir in Cornwall, in the extreme south-west of England, where it stayed from November 1992 to March 1993. It reappeared at another reservoir near by in April 1994 and bred with a Little Grebe, the pair rearing three hybrid young. The male disappeared in September. At least one of the hybrid young survived through the winter but it was not seen after March 1995. This has remained the only known instance of a Pied-billed Grebe breeding on the European side of the Atlantic, albeit hybridizing with another species. Although hybridization with the closely related Atitlán Grebe is thought to have taken place, and contributed to that grebe's extinction (*see* the species account below), this is the only recorded instance of the Pied-billed Grebe hybridizing with the Little Grebe. This reinforces the view that the two species have evolved from a common ancestor, sharing as they do several similarities in their display behaviour, which were obviously sufficiently similar to enable a male Pied-billed Grebe to attract a female Little Grebe.

Most of the early records of Pied-billed Grebes on the European side of the Atlantic were in autumn, a time when birds of many other species, migrating south down the eastern seaboard of North America, get blown across the Atlantic. In recent years there have been a number of spring records, too. If this trend continues, together with increasing numbers, then it may not be too long before two of these vagrants meet up and breed somewhere in western Europe. This has already happened in Hawaii, where the first record occurred in 1974. Two birds wintered there in 1983–1984, and what was probably the same pair in 1984–1985, mirroring the habit in Britain of returning after an absence. In summer 1985, the pair bred and one or more pairs have bred every year since.

The bill of the Pied-billed Grebe is an altogether stouter affair than any other grebe, apart from the extinct Atitlán Grebe. It is less the pointed stabbing bill common to many species, but rather a deep, crushing tool. The power of the bill and its associated muscles enables the grebe to feed on large crustaceans and spiny fish which the other species cannot manage. Crayfish form an important part of its diet and the grebe is quite capable of crushing their hard shells in its bill. It has evolved a technique for removing the two main claws by holding the crayfish by each in turn and shaking it vigorously to break the claws off. While most birds tend to swallow their prey head first, the grebe swallows crayfish tail first. This is the direction in which the animal swims and is more streamlined. With the main claws removed, the tail and remaining legs become folded forwards in the mouth and throat, making swallowing easier. Spiny catfish are dealt with by repeated biting and pinching, damaging not only the spines but also the internal organs. A fish may be bitten, dropped, picked up again and bitten some more, before the grebe eventually eats it, head first this time.

Pied-billed Grebes are aggressive birds, not just towards each other when breeding, but towards other species, too. The nest territories are not very large, but may be defended year-round in sedentary populations. It is usually the male on his own that keeps other Pied-billed Grebes away, though the female may sometimes

37

join in. A typical form of attack is to dive and swim towards the intruder, coming up underneath and pecking at its belly and feet underwater. This is usually enough to send it fleeing. Indeed, some birds, and not just grebes, turn tail and swim or fly away rapidly as soon as the male dives towards them. The migrant grebes, outside the breeding season, are more tolerant of each other and may gather in substantial flocks when on migration and during the winter. Over 20,000 have been seen on the Salton Sea in southern California in late autumn.

Somewhat surprisingly, there are no estimates of population size for the Pied-billed Grebe in the United States and Canada. It is not regarded as being as common as the Black-necked Grebe, which numbers over one million, but is far more widespread and could easily be numbered in hundreds of thousands. The South American race has been estimated to lie in the 10,000–25,000 bracket, based on some sample surveys and comparing its abundance with that of other species. The Antillean race is clearly scarcer than this, but there is no information as to numbers or trends – something that should be put right before too long. The only apparent threats against this species come from egg-collecting for food in some parts of its tropical range. It does not appear to be hunted to any extent. It is in most ways an adaptable and successful bird, more than able to hold its own against other waterbirds on its chosen wetlands.

ATITLÁN GREBE

PODILYMBUS GIGAS

— Formerly found on Lake Atitlán, Guatemala.

THE ATITLÁN GREBE IS EXTINCT. IT WAS KNOWN TO science for a mere 60 years from 1929, when it was first described as a full species. By about 1990 the last known birds had died.

At up to 50cm (20in) in length, this was a large grebe; indeed other common names include Giant Grebe and Giant Pied-billed Grebe. The latter reveals the species' origins: it is assumed to have evolved from the Pied-billed Grebe (it was first described as a subspecies of the Pied-billed Grebe in 1862), and has both grown larger and become flightless in the process. Why this should have happened on just one large lake (130sq km/50 sq miles), in the highlands of Guatemala, lying at 1,555m (5,100ft) above sea level, is unknown, but there are plenty of other examples among birds, and other taxa, where isolation has led to considerable morphological adaptations. The increase in size may have enabled the bird to dive more deeply and stay down longer, thus reducing the competition for food with other inhabitants of the lake, while flightlessness is often a development that takes place in the absence of predators.

At the time of the Atitlán Grebe's discovery, there were estimated to be about 100 pairs, mainly confined to the sheltered southern shore of the lake, where the most abundant reed-beds, in which the birds nested, occurred. Surveys in 1936 and 1960 confirmed the size of the population at between 250 and 300 birds and it was suggested that this represented the optimum carrying capacity of the lake.

The uniqueness of the grebe was recognized as early as the mid-1950s when the lake was made a National Park. The grebe was protected in 1959, by presidential decree. This prohibited hunting of not just the grebes but all other waterbirds, though some subsistence hunting of coots and other gallinules was allowed to continue. However, the late 1950s brought two adverse developments. Firstly, the local people began extensive reed-cutting to supply a mat-making industry, and did so without regard to a sustainable harvest. Secondly, the lake began to be

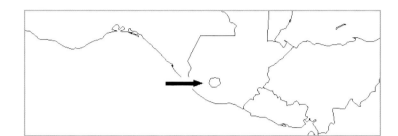

promoted as a tourist resort by, among others, the former airline Pan American. One of the advertised attractions of the lake was the fishing, despite the fact that the lake contained nothing suitable in the way of sporting fish! In order to remedy this, about 2,000 bass fingerlings were introduced between 1958 and 1960. These have the potential to grow to over 10kg (22lb). Unfortunately, this introduction decimated the indigenous crabs and small fish in the lake, the latter the main food of the grebes. Of 19 indigenous species of fish in the lake in the mid-1960s, only six could be found ten years later. And the bass did not eat just the fish, but as they grew they started to take grebe chicks, too.

In the mid-1960s, a remarkable lady, Anne LaBastille, appeared on the scene. She became interested in the grebes and quickly realized that they were in difficulties; she could find only 80 individuals in 1965. Virtually single-handedly, she set about finding funds for a refuge, badgering officials to increase habitat protection and generally raising awareness of the Atitlán Grebe, both around the lake and further afield, involving not just the Guatemalan government, but international bodies such as WWF. Her efforts were rewarded by the appointment of wardens, along with regulations preventing reed harvesting during the breeding season and making the harvesting more sustainable by limiting the percentage that could be cut in a year. In addition, many of the bass were removed and large numbers of small native species introduced. Steps were taken to explain to the local people why these measures had been put in place and to try to engage their interest in the grebe.

39

Chris Rose

In 1968 a 2-hectare (5-acre) fenced refuge was created. Two pairs of grebes were captured and placed inside. These bred readily, but gales and wave action eventually tore open the fence and they escaped. However, all the above measures, perhaps coupled with the birds' ability to adapt to living with the remaining bass, led to a welcome recovery in numbers of grebes to about 200 by 1973 and 232 in 1975.

Sadly, just as the situation looked more rosy, a new man-made threat appeared, and two natural events had a catastrophic effect. The man-made threat was the spread of first holiday homes and then hotels along the lake shore, built by and for people from Guatemala City. Each house or hotel owner wanted their own stretch of beach. This led to a considerable increase in the clearance of the reedbeds. Piers and boat-houses were built, and large numbers of pleasure and fishing boats were using the lake. The natural events were, firstly, the colonization of the lake by the Pied-billed Grebe and, secondly, an earthquake.

The first Pied-billed Grebe was collected at Lake Atitlán in 1964, while by the late 1960s there were several breeding pairs. These new arrivals became competitors for the fish that formed the main food of the Atitlán Grebe at a time when the total small fish resource had already been reduced by the introduction of the bass. Potentially much more serious was the possibility that the two species may have begun to hybridize, a process which, if it became commonplace, could only have one ending: the loss of the Atitlán Grebe as a separate species. In 1976, a massive earthquake occurred in Guatemala, killing many thousands of people. The effect on the lake was a steady drop in water level which eventually reached 6m (20ft), exposing large areas of shore and leaving the reedbeds high and dry. Anne LaBastille and her co-workers organized the transplanting of tens of thousands of clumps of bulrushes and cat-tails to the new waterline but, by 1980, only 130 grebes could be found.

The political situation became very fraught during this period and in 1982 one of the key people promoting the conservation of the grebes was murdered by guerrillas. Illegal hunting increased while habitat deterioration accelerated. By the mid-1980s it was estimated that the emergent vegetation had declined by at least 60 per cent, not just depriving the grebes of their safe nesting sites, but removing a vital natural filtration system which kept the lake water reasonably free of pollution from agricultural run-off. Since large areas of the land exposed by the drop in water level following the earthquake had been turned over to farmland, this lack was even more noticeable.

The decline and disappearance of the Atitlán Grebe now became almost inevitable. By 1984, the population had fallen to about 50 and a trial attempt was made to introduce the grebe to another lake, by taking two eggs and placing them in grebe nests there. Only one egg hatched and the chick probably died when a few days old.

Finally, in 1986, it was decided to try to round up the remaining 32 birds and place them in a specially fenced reserve. Apart from its larger size and proportionately larger bill, the Atitlán Grebe was extremely similar in plumage to the Pied-billed Grebe and identification at a distance was a distinct problem during the last few years. At any rate, as the round-up was being attempted, about a dozen of the birds took flight – they were either Pied-billed Grebes or hybrids. The last four grebes were seen in 1989. They may have been pure, but if, as seems possible, they were hybrids, then extinction as a separate species had probably taken place a year or two before.

While there was still a thriving population of Atitlán Grebes on the lake, Anne LaBastille studied them in considerable detail. She found that the birds paired for life and held life-long territories based around their chosen area of reed-bed. They were accomplished divers, capable of staying underwater for up to 90 seconds during which time they might travel 90m (300ft). When defending their territory, chasing away other grebes, or when disturbed by a boat, the grebes would rise up and patter over the surface, flapping their stunted wings vigorously, and attaining a speed of nearly 7kph (over 4mph), which they could sustain for up to 100m (330ft) or even more. Sadly, neither this striking behaviour nor their pirouetting courtship displays will ever be seen again.

41

WHITE-TUFTED GREBE

ROLLANDIA ROLLAND

— LAKE JUNÍN RACE *R.r.morrisoni*: Confined to Lake Junín, Peru.
— FALKLAND ISLANDS RACE *R.r.rolland*: Resident on Falkland Islands.
— CHILEAN RACE *R.r.chilensis*: Widespread on South American mainland from Tierra del Fuego north to north-east Peru and southern Brazil.

TWO OF THE THREE RACES OF THE WHITE-TUFTED GREBE have reasonably secure populations, but the Lake Junín race has been declining rapidly in recent years and must be regarded as seriously threatened. The account of the Lake Junín Flightless Grebe (*see* page 79) tells the story of the mining pollution that afflicts the lake and the dramatic effect that it has had on numbers of that grebe. One possible further adverse factor that has been suggested is competition with the White-tufted Grebe on the lake, but this species, too, is in trouble, so a conflict of this nature seems unlikely. The White-tufted Grebes totalled around 4,000 in 1977, had dropped to little more than half that, at 2,150, only four years later in 1981, while by the mid-1990s the population amounted to little more than 500 birds. Large-scale mortality has been observed during drought years. The problems of Lake Junín are affecting all the waterbirds living there, not just the Flightless Grebe. It has been suggested that the White-tufted Grebes on all the mountain lakes in Peru and Bolivia are of this race, which is distinguished by a larger, heavier bill, but more recent work confirms that it is confined to Lake Junín.

The Falkland Islands race is also not numerous, with no more than about 500 pairs, but the population appears to be stable and is widely dispersed, so it is not seriously threatened in any way. Birds of this race are much larger than those of the other two, and the race has been suggested as a separate species. It is sedentary on the Falklands and no birds from the mainland are thought to visit the islands.

A total of about 100,000 birds has been attributed to the third race, though this is not much more than an educated guess. Certainly the White-tufted Grebe of mainland South America is both widespread and abundant in some areas. It occurs from sea-level to high in the mountains, on lakes at altitudes up to 4,500m (14,750ft). There are counts of up to 5,000 on a number of different wetlands in Argentina, and numbers also run into thousands on mountain lakes further north, for example on Lake Titicaca and on other lakes in southern Peru.

A feature of the White-tufted Grebe is the wide diversity of waters that it selects for nesting. It breeds not only on the very large South American wetlands, such as Lakes Titicaca and Junín, hundreds of square kilometres in extent, but also on tiny ponds, roadside ditches and even slow-flowing rivers. Some of these waters are only temporary, formed during rains and drying up in droughts. However, the grebe is adaptable enough to be able to move on to larger, permanent, waters when this occurs. Outside the breeding season, the grebes from the southern parts of Chile and Argentina move north and make for the coasts, living in large flocks in sheltered bays and fjords, often associated with large beds of seaweed.

The White-tufted Grebe has a courtship display not found in any other species, called the 'bumping ceremony'.

42

Chris Rose

During the ceremony the birds bump into each other deliberately, something which is unusual in any birds. Jon Fjeldså was the first to describe it in detail. The ceremony may start with the pair displaying on the surface, swimming with necks stretched upwards and making soft calls. Perhaps more usually, two apparently unpaired grebes will swim towards each other and then, while still 10–15m (33–50ft) apart, both birds dive and apparently meet under water, turn to face the same direction and re-emerge swimming side by side. This part of the display ends with the birds circling each other, again with the necks stretched up and the crests and ear-coverts raised. After further posturing, sometimes turning the heads slowly, sometimes quickly, one bird dives and deliberately comes up underneath the other one, bumping it with its breast. Both birds then rear up almost vertically in the water, breasts touching, treading water briefly. The bumping may be repeated, before the birds relax, sometimes swimming away from each other, sometimes moving on to a weed ceremony, which is common to other species. Jon Fjeldså concluded that the bumping ceremony was a ritualized form of aggression – diving towards an opponent being the commonest form of attack in grebes. Here, the pair are actually courting, and the courtship element of the two grebes so close to each other overcomes the urge to fight.

The need to subsume aggressive behaviour into courtship is important in the White-tufted Grebe as it is a territorial species, very rarely breeding in colonies like several other species, and then only in small groups containing a handful of pairs. These grebes usually take up, and defend, quite large territories around their nests. In an area of uniform aquatic vegetation, nests were found to be spaced over 60m (200ft) apart, with even the closest at a distance of at least 30m (100ft). In well-vegetated areas, the pair feed and rear their young almost entirely within the territory. Where the marshy vegetation is more scattered, they may move outside the territory to feed. In suitable parts of the range, perhaps especially in the north, the grebes will breed at almost any time of the year and will have two or three broods within the year. Pairs behaving like this will hold on to their territory more or less continuously. Even when unpaired or outside a defined breeding season, these grebes remain much less gregarious than many other species, most often staying well spread out, whether feeding or resting, up to 20m (66ft) apart. Whenever birds do swim or drift towards each other, as soon as they come within a few metres of each other, aggressive interactions are likely. Threats and chasing ensue until the birds disperse to more acceptable distances and calm is restored. Interestingly, there seems to be very little interaction between the White-tufted Grebe and any other species occupying the same waters. The aggression is solely within the species.

Although the White-tufted Grebe is a reasonably accomplished diver, capable of staying down for over 30 seconds, only a part of its food is obtained by underwater pursuit. In the main, it swims among floating plants, or just above underwater vegetation, with its head submerged to above the eyes, swinging it from side to side and peering into the vegetation for invertebrates, then pecking them from among the leaves. This near-surface feeding is combined with up-ending and brief dives, presumably to pick up otherwise out-of-reach prey.

This delightful small grebe – the only one with tufts of white feathers on a black head – is certainly not threatened as a species, but the Lake Junín race is under serious threat and its survival, along with that of the Junín Flightless Grebe, will depend on appropriate action being taken in the very near future.

TITICACA FLIGHTLESS GREBE

ROLLANDIA MICROPTERA

— Found on a small number of high altitude lakes in south-eastern Peru and western Bolivia.

THE PRINCIPAL HOME OF THE TITICACA FLIGHTLESS Grebe is Lake Titicaca, the huge freshwater lake that straddles the Peruvian-Bolivian border with about half its area in each country, together with the neighbouring Peruvian lakes of Arapa and Umayo, and south about 300km (185 miles) into Bolivia to Lakes Uru-uru and Poopo. This grebe has clearly evolved, along with the White-tufted Grebe, from some common ancestor probably dating back to a separation in the Pleistocene, from several hundred thousand to as long as a million years ago. Unlike the two other flightless grebes, the Atitlán and the Junín, the Titicaca managed to establish itself on more than one lake, though it should be noted that all are interconnected by watercourses and although the River Desaguadero flowing out of Lake Titicaca all the way to Lakes Uru-uru and Poopo is generally very shallow, this may not have been the case in past millennia.

The total population of the Titicaca Flightless Grebe is probably in the low thousands. There is general agreement that there are more than 2,000, but the upper figure is unknown and could be double or treble that number. Counting the birds on Lake Titicaca is not easy because the water surface covers an amazingly large area of about 8,300sq km (3,200sq miles). The huge mountain lake lies at an altitude of 3,800m (12,500ft). It has a maximum depth of 283m (928ft), and its extensive shallows and adjoining marshes have enormous areas of associated emergent vegetation. The most striking plant is giant totara reed *Schoenoplecus totara* which can reach up to 7m (23ft) tall. When it drifts away from the shore, it can form floating islands so large, and stable, that the local native tribespeople, the Uro, actually live on them while fishing. The reed is harvested to make boats and is cut when young as food for cattle. As the reed-beds form an important shelter for the grebes, there are

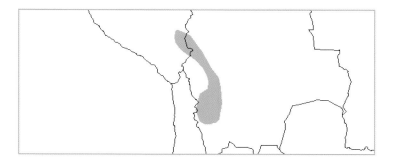

concerns about over-harvesting in some areas. Pollution and the high level of boat traffic associated with the town of Puno have eliminated the grebe from this part of the lake, but it seems to be doing well elsewhere, including on Lakes Arapa and Umayo, although on the latter some birds have died after being caught in fishing nets.

Lake Poopo, on the other hand, faces considerable problems and the population of grebes there has come under recent threats. Another large lake, about 2,500sq km (956sq miles) in extent, Poopo is very shallow, rarely more than 3m (10ft) in depth. It is a saline lake, lacking any outlet except in times of flood, and in recent years control of the River Desaguadero at its outlet from Lake Titicaca has led to drying up of the lake, while silting of the river has actually caused it to flood back and create Lake Uru-uru, a short distance to the north. In February 2000, a major oil spill threatened both Lakes Uru-uru and Poopo, when an oil pipeline was ruptured by a flash flood and nearly 30,000 gallons of refined oil and petrol was allowed to flow into the River Desaguadero. It was several days before any clean-up began and local people reported that the oil had not only reached Lake Poopo about 150km (95 miles) downstream, but had killed all the wildlife there. Despite this, very few oiled birds were picked up and surveys some months later revealed very little sign of oil pollution in the lake. Its effect on the grebes is as yet unknown, but the incident

Chris Rose

is a clear demonstration of the threats faced by a flightless bird living on a handful of lakes.

In terms of population survival, the Titicaca Flightless Grebe has one characteristic in its favour, namely its ability to breed all the year round. It has no defined breeding season, but instead nests whenever conditions, probably including water-level and associated vegetation and food availability, become favourable. It is also capable of breeding more than once in a year, and it is possible to see adult birds with small chicks from their present brood accompanied by full-grown young from the previous one. There is evidence that this breeding strategy has helped the grebe recover quite quickly from years of drought which can prevent breeding and cause a drop in numbers.

The Titicaca Flightless Grebe is territorial during the breeding season, nesting only occasionally in very loose aggregations which hardly qualify as colonies. Most pairs adopt and defend territories, whose centres are up to 50m (165ft) apart. The closest distance ever recorded between two nests is 10m (33ft). The nests are normally placed in tall reeds not far from open water. On Lake Umayo, where all the reed-beds appeared to be occupied by nesting pairs, some nests were placed among floating water-weed.

When feeding, during the breeding season or outside it, the grebes remain dispersed, and choose both shallows, with depths up to 3m (10ft), and deeper areas, to 10m (33ft) or even more. In the latter, though, there is always underwater weed in which the birds find their food. It has been estimated that fish, which the birds take up to a maximum size of 15cm (6in), make up as much as 98 per cent by weight of their diet. Titicaca Flightless Grebes are accomplished divers and can reach speeds of up to 1m (3.3ft) per second underwater, staying down for as long as 40 seconds and making repeated dives with pauses of no more than 15 seconds in between. The principal fish that they catch do not live in shoals, so the birds spread out to feed since there is no advantage in several birds diving together.

The Lake Titicaca basin, including the entire water area and the surrounding marshland, was declared a Ramsar site in 1997–1998 by both Peru and Bolivia. This gives it protected status under the international convention for the protection of wetlands and waterfowl. The two countries are implementing joint conservation and management plans to ensure that the lake is maintained in as good a condition as possible, with associated regulation of pollution and water use. It is hoped to institute regular monitoring of the wildlife and their habitats, which should help to safeguard the Titicaca Flightless Grebe and prevent it heading for extinction as has already been the fate of the Atitlán Grebe and is a distinct possibility for the Junín Grebe.

HOARY-HEADED GREBE

POLIOCEPHALUS POLIOCEPHALUS

— Found in Australia, including Tasmania, and in South Island, New Zealand.

THE HOARY-HEADED GREBE TAKES ITS NAME FROM THE fine silvery-white streaking on its black head, which make the bird look not only grey-haired or 'hoary', but also exactly as if someone had brushed these feathers and sleeked them back neatly and tidily over its cheeks and crown and down the sides of the neck. The feathers to the sides of the head are not raised much, if at all, in display, but the crown feathers may be lifted to give the head an almost peaked appearance as well as making it look very narrow, as if squashed from side to side. This species is confined to Australia and, since only 1975, New Zealand, where it is very scarce. The first scattering of records for New Zealand included a pair which bred in the winter of 1975–1976 in South Island. Breeding was repeated in the following two years, with two pairs in 1977–1978, but since then, although there have been annual records of ones and twos, no further nesting has been proved. It remains uncertain whether the continued trickle of records comes from birds arriving occasionally from Australia, or whether a few pairs have become established and are perhaps being overlooked among the New Zealand Grebes of North Island.

In Australia, the Hoary-headed Grebe is common and widespread, especially in the south and south-east, and in the south-west. The population has been estimated at around 500,000 birds, a similar figure to the Australasian Grebe. The two species are also generally similar in their choice of habitat, breeding on a wide variety of shallow wetlands, including large, temporary floods, as well as farm ponds and reservoirs. The Hoary-headed Grebe is not confined to freshwater, being able to live on brackish or saline lakes, too. It favours larger, open waters with plenty of submerged weed for breeding, but seems to avoid stands of dense emergent vegetation. At other times of the year it can be found in large flocks on coastal

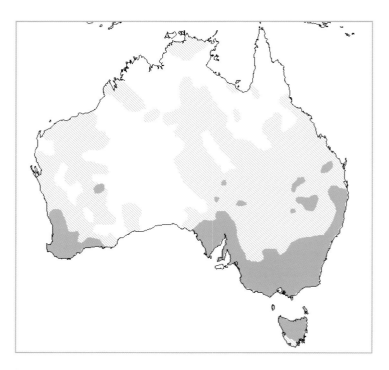

lagoons, tidal estuaries and even sheltered sea bays. Like the Australasian Grebe, it will take advantage of temporary wetlands following rains, spreading far and wide across the country, well into Queensland and Northern Territory. However, it is less likely to use temporary waters for breeding, utilizing them instead for feeding on the abundant aquatic invertebrates that they may contain.

The Hoary-headed Grebe is one of the most gregarious of all the grebes, certainly when breeding. Many colonies comprise between 100 and 300 (or occasionally up to 400) pairs. In such colonies, the nests are placed in dense clusters, each consisting of several nests perhaps 1m (3ft) apart forming a floating raft among the waterweed. However, not all the birds breed in colonies. Single pairs nest on small waters, while in some places there may be several pairs in the same area, but with the nests much more spaced out. Unlike the Australasian Grebe, and again confirming that it does not respond in the same way to intermittent rains,

the Hoary-headed Grebe's breeding season seems to be shorter, with most nesting taking place between September and December. This shorter season also reflects the fact that the species is single-brooded. For such a relatively common and widespread species, the Hoary-headed Grebe's basic breeding biology is poorly known, with no precise measurements of either incubation or fledging period. Its displays have been studied, revealing that it is one of the quietest of the grebes, uttering only quite soft calls even in the most vigorous of its courtship or territorial displays. Perhaps in such a gregarious species, the calls need only be audible at relatively close range.

Outside the breeding season, the grebes remain in flocks, often up to many thousands strong. There are records of non-breeding flocks of 2,000–3,000, and once 4,900 were counted together just after the end of the breeding season. Within these flocks, the birds typically stay close together, whether resting or feeding. It is quite usual to see two or three birds actually touching each other as they preen or rest. It is possible that these are pairs or family members, but in fact the pair bond is not thought to be maintained after the end of the nesting period. Roosting birds, too, may sleep in physical contact with each other. The flock generally moves into an area of waterweed, which prevents them drifting when asleep, and forms into tight groups of 20 or 30 birds occupying an area of perhaps only 2–3sq m (20–30sq ft), with birds frequently touching several others within the group. Such bodily contact is relatively unusual in the bird world, and certainly among grebes.

Like some other species of grebe, Hoary-headed Grebes often indulge in communal diving when feeding. This helps the birds locate prey and increases feeding opportunities as one bird flushes food items towards another. Detailed observations of a feeding flock in New South Wales showed that about one-quarter of the feeding grebes were less than 1m (3ft) apart while three-quarters of them were no more than 5m (17ft) from the next grebe. The principal food is aquatic arthropods, especially the adults and nymphs of water beetles, bugs, midges, caddisflies and

dragonflies, together with water snails and various crustaceans, such as shrimps. This varied diet is obtained almost exclusively by diving, during which the birds stay under water for an average of 17.5 seconds. The grebes may dive many times in quick succession, with only a brief pause on the surface in between. They have been observed underwater, paddling strongly with their feet, holding themselves near vertically and pecking continuously among the water-weeds or in the bottom sediments. Virtually all the food is consumed underwater, only the largest items being brought to the surface to be dealt with.

The dive to obtain food is relatively clumsy, preceded by a distinct jump followed by a splashy submergence. However, when danger threatens, perhaps from a passing bird of prey, the grebe can launch itself rapidly and smoothly forwards and downwards in a single movement, propelled by the kicking feet. The Hoary-headed Grebe appears to fly more than other grebes, both (uncommon among other species) to escape from danger, and to move from one part of a wetland to another. Most grebes will swim many hundreds of metres to another area, but the Hoary-headed Grebe readily takes to the air when the distance it wants to travel is more than, perhaps, 200m (650ft). Some of the movements the birds make can be classed as migration, taking them annually from inland breeding areas to the coast for the winter. Other flights are clearly more dispersive, following rains, while there may also be moult migrations, when the birds gather in suitable waters for the period of post-breeding flightlessness. One ringing recovery recorded a distance of 572km (355 miles), while the birds that turned up in New Zealand in the 1970s had moved at least 1,500–2,000km (930–1,240 miles), though with the opportunity for landing on the sea on the way. There is a report of a pair which landed at night on a boat in the Bass Strait, between Victoria and Tasmania.

The Hoary-headed Grebe has a substantial population which is sufficiently widespread and adaptable not to be threatened, except in a very local way. Its ability to utilize artificial wetlands, such as ponds and reservoirs, offsets the loss of other wetlands to drainage or development.

NEW ZEALAND GREBE

POLIOCEPHALUS RUFOPECTUS

— Found only on North Island, New Zealand. Formerly on South Island.

THE NEW ZEALAND GREBE IS A CLOSE RELATIVE OF THE Hoary-headed Grebe, with similar, though not so white, 'brushed-back' head feathers. The foreneck and breast are reddish and the underparts much darker. The species is endemic to New Zealand where it is now confined to North Island, though it formerly occurred on South Island, too. The reasons for its disappearance from South Island are something of a mystery. When first recorded, it appeared to be quite widespread, if nowhere common. There have been no apparent major changes to available wetlands, and no reason why it should have suffered more from the attentions of introduced predators here than in North Island. However, a sharp reduction in numbers and range was already apparent in the latter part of the 19th century. This continued into the first half of the 20th century, by which time the bird was confined mainly to lakes in Fiordland and West Coast. The last few were seen in the mid-1960s, since when the occasional sighting has been assumed to be of a straggler from North Island.

The population of New Zealand Grebes on North Island is estimated to be between 1,200 and 1,500. Numbers appear to be at least stable and possibly increasing in a few areas. Like other grebes, it has suffered from the drainage and deterioration of many natural wetlands, but has benefited at least as much from the creation of artificial waters, especially farm reservoirs and flight ponds. It has also proved quite tolerant of human disturbance, breeding alongside built-up areas on at least one large lake. Although the grebe is protected, there are reports of it being shot by hunters, even when it is swimming on the water, though other sources say that it is ignored by hunters and not badly disturbed by shooting on the same water.

The grebes breed in territories, with solitary pairs on small ponds, but several pairs, well spaced out, on larger waters. After the breeding season, the birds gather on relatively few larger lakes to spend the autumn and

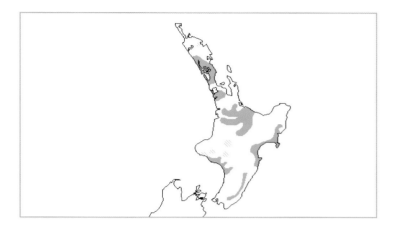

winter, sometimes in flocks numbering a few hundred, so comprising a very significant proportion of the total population. Obviously, this is the period of maximum vulnerability for the species and it must help that one or two key wetlands have been protected from shooting. It is not known how far the grebes will move from breeding grounds to wintering flocks, but it is noticeable that the few recent records from South Island have all been during mid-winter immediately after the birds have moved into flocks on North Island. Furthermore, it is thought that the population in the south of North Island is increasing and that the birds in that area are perhaps more mobile than those further north. If the population continues to increase it is at least possible that a natural recolonization of South Island might take place before too long.

The courtship of the New Zealand Grebe has been studied in some detail. Like the related Hoary-headed Grebe, this species is not very vocal during its displays and the calls it does make are a matter of some disagreement between observers. The classic late 19th-century work, Buller's *A History of the Birds of New Zealand*, states that the adults issue a shrill, sibilant whistle and that this is where its Maori name of Weweia arises. Two more recent books on New Zealand birds also say that the bird has a whistling 'wee-we-we' call. However, when two ornithologists, several years apart, devoted much

time to studying the grebe's courtship and breeding behaviour, neither of them heard any such call, which leaves a small mystery waiting to be solved. Certainly, when the pair is courting, only the softest of guttural calls is given.

The most frequent of the birds' displays is called the 'patter ceremony' because it is accompanied by the sound of their feet pattering on the water. It is performed throughout the breeding season, most often when the pair come together after seeing off an intruder. They swim around and about each other with their heads held low, and jerking to and fro, but the wings raised, still closed, above their backs. Their white rear-ends are raised, too, which reveals a circular pattern either side of the tail, like a pair of eyes. Suddenly, one bird rises up slightly in the water and rushes away from the other one, pattering noisily and splashily with its feet, before subsiding into a glide. Its mate may follow it, or may just stay back and watch. Another, less frequent, display is the 'diving ceremony' which starts with the birds close together and facing each other. One bird dives, passes under the other bird and re-emerges behind it, causing it to spin round to keep it in sight. Perhaps the most spectacular action by these grebes is the crash-dive that they do when badly alarmed, perhaps by a bird of prey swooping down on them. The haste of the dive is such that the grebe's breast pushes down into the water before its head, sending a jet of water up to 1m (3ft 3in) into the air. It is possible that this is a deliberate action to confuse and put off the predator.

Although the great majority of New Zealand Grebe nests consist of the typical platform of waterweed anchored among aquatic vegetation, there are a number of records of unusual sites. Nests have been found on a small ledge of soil close to the water, in a small cave and in a boatshed! On one lake, nests were recorded in old motor tyres being used as fenders on jetties. The two or three eggs are incubated by both parents, who also both look after the young, feeding them while they are small. When the young from the first clutch are no more than two to three weeks old, the female starts a second clutch, but the young will continue to be looked after by the non-incubating bird, even though by this time they are beginning to feed themselves. There is a record of a pair on a farm reservoir producing no less than four broods in a prolonged season which started in July and continued until February.

Hatching success and brood survival is higher on small ponds and reservoirs than on larger waters. Both variation in water-levels and wave action can have damaging consequences for nests, and these tend to be reduced on smaller waters. Grebes in such places may also suffer less disturbance from other waterbirds and potential predators. This may, indeed, help to explain the species' survival on North Island and its disappearance from South Island. The development in recent years of lots of small waters suitable for breeding has enabled the grebe to do well on North Island. Here the species has been able to overcome any problems caused by the disappearance of larger waters, or of low breeding success on those that remain. Such problems could perhaps have contributed to its disappearance from South Island. It is encouraging to speculate that the creation of high-quality replacement habitat is helping this grebe, with its very small population, and may lead in time to its breeding on South Island once more.

GREAT GREBE
PODICEPS MAJOR

— ARGENTINE RACE *P.m.major*: Paraguay and south-east Brazil south to Patagonia and central Chile; also north-west Peru.
— CHILEAN RACE *P.m.navasi*: Southern Chile south to Tierra del Fuego.
— The isolated population in north-west Peru is sometimes considered a separate race. The Chilean race is separated by its larger size and blacker head, but is not universally accepted.

THE GREAT GREBE, AS ITS NAME IMPLIES, IS THE LARGEST of the grebe family, slightly longer and quite a lot heavier than the Western Grebe of North America. It spends more time on salt water than any other grebe, only coming to inland freshwaters to breed. The principal wintering areas are along the coast, usually in shallow, often rocky areas, in estuaries and bays on the Atlantic coast and in the fjord systems of the Pacific coast of Chile, where it makes use of the large kelp beds. Flocks of several hundred birds gather in such places, concentrated in areas where there are shoals of fish, including silversides, *Odonthestes*, which can be abundant. Here the grebes sometimes feed alongside cormorants, but competition appears to be slight because the grebes tend to take smaller fish.

The Great Grebe has been described as the finest diver of the family, springing upwards and forwards in an elegant arch out of the water, and re-entering with a minimum of splashing. This diving technique is probably an adaptation to feeding in open water among waves. Dives usually take place into the wind. Underwater, this grebe is capable of longer dives than other species, covering up to 50m (165ft) before re-emerging. Its main food is fish, mainly around 2–5cm (1–2in) long, though up to a maximum of about 10cm (4in). The fish are caught between the mandibles, unlike the Western Grebe which can spear its prey. Although the Great Grebe's bill is even longer and more dagger-like, it lacks the Western Grebe's specialized neck and bill characteristics which permit this. Other foods include molluscs and crustaceans, including small crabs. In freshwater it will also take insects and has been recorded taking the young of other waterbirds such as coots.

Nesting is colonial, often in quite dense colonies. One in Chile had between 150 and 200 nests in an area of

about 2,000sq m (20,000sq ft). The nest platforms in this colony, probably typical for the species, were built of and anchored to emergent vegetation in marshes close to the delta mouths of rivers flowing into a large lake. The marshes extended from the very gently sloping shoreline many metres out into the water, leaving a channel of water down the centre which gave the grebes access to the main lake. The timing of nesting and the choice of nesting area was closely tied to water level. Breeding began in September and continued into January. However, in the middle of the latter month, the water level in the nesting area started to drop. A month later, it had fallen by half, from about 1.6m (5ft 3in) to 0.8m (2ft 8in). This left the nests in such shallow water that the grebes could no longer dive to escape danger. It also exposed a wide stony mudflat between the nesting area and the open water. This was more than the grebes

(as inefficient on land as all their relatives) were prepared to cross, so those still incubating abandoned their eggs. Breeding started up again at the same site the following July after the water level had risen again to about 2.4m (7ft 10in).

Considering that Great Grebes are moving regularly between inland freshwater breeding grounds and wintering quarters on the coast, one might expect a fairly regularly timed breeding season. In fact it is quite variable. Some populations apparently nest in any month of the year, while others are more concentrated in the southern summer, from October to January or February. To what extent the birds may prospect for suitable nesting grounds or visit their traditional site to test whether conditions are suitable is not known. With clutches of three to five eggs and second broods quite common, these grebes have a significant ability to take advantage of good conditions and thus offset the occasions when they have to abandon a breeding attempt because of dropping water levels.

The population of Great Grebes in north-west Peru is something of a mystery as it was only discovered breeding there in the 1990s. Before then, it was known that small numbers of grebes occurred in the area, but they were almost all seen on the coast and were assumed to be accidental vagrants from further south, the nearest birds in northern Chile being, perhaps, 2,000km (1,240 miles) away. However, regular counts

in the 1980s suggested a sedentary population occupying coastal bays and estuaries, especially those with bordering marshes. Numbers were up to 68 in one locality. Finally, breeding was confirmed on two lagoons and it is now regarded as important to discover the exact extent of this small population, its range and its ability to sustain itself. Preliminary observations suggest that these birds may on average be rather smaller than those to the south, raising the possibility that they belong to a separate subspecies. This would also indicate that they have been isolated for a very long time but have been overlooked. because of their small numbers and relatively remote coastal haunts.

The Peruvian population of the Great Grebe is clearly very small, perhaps only a few hundred individuals. It has been estimated that the total population in southern South America is around 50,000 individuals, though how this is divided between the two subspecies is not known. If the Peruvian population of the Great Grebe was initially thought to consist of accidental occurrences from further south, this would fit with the half dozen sightings of birds on the Falklands, presumably wandering, or unwillingly blown there, from the mainland coast. However, two specimens in Spanish museums, originally claimed as genuine vagrants, are now dismissed as wrongly, or even fraudulently, labelled. One is said to have been collected near Barcelona in February 1908 and the second in Valencia between 1900 and 1910.

RED-NECKED GREBE

PODICEPS GRISEGENA

— WESTERN PALEARCTIC RACE *P.g.grisegena*: Breeds north-west Europe to south-west Asia, including Pakistan and India, wintering on coasts of north-west Europe, Mediterranean, Black, Caspian and Aral Seas.
— PACIFIC RACE *P.g.holboellii*: North-eastern Asia, mainly Russia and Japan, and north-western North America from Alaska to central Canada and north-west United States, wintering on the Pacific coasts of Asia and North America and, to a lesser extent, the Atlantic coast of North America.
— Races separated on size.

THREE GREBES, THE HORNED, THE BLACK-NECKED AND the Red-necked, occur both in eastern Asia and in western North America, but of these only the Red-necked appears to have spread comparatively recently to both sides of the Pacific from a single centre. The first two species have been apart for long enough to have evolved as separate subspecies in Asia and in North America. It is true that there are small differences between the Red-necked in the two regions (those in North America have slightly larger bills than those in Asia), but these have been deemed insufficient to classify them as subspecies. There are also minor measurement differences within the Red-necked Grebes of the western Palearctic, with the birds of northern Finland and Russia having longer, thinner bills and very slightly longer wings and legs than those elsewhere in Europe and western Asia. Another point, potentially of greater taxonomic significance, is the apparent lack of any difference in measurements between the sexes in *grisegena* whereas it is quite apparent in *holboellii*. This led at one time to the two subspecies being proposed as separate species, but longer series of measurements showed that male and female *grisegena* differed in bill size though in other measurements the sexual dimorphism was not as pronounced as in *holboellii*. There is no plumage difference between the sexes in either subspecies.

Grebes sit at the top of a food chain and therefore, like other predators, can be used as indicators of the state of health of their habitat, in most cases fertile freshwaters. Thus, if numbers of grebes breeding or wintering on a particular wetland start to decline, this may be an indication of the failure of their food supply or of a die-back in the essential aquatic vegetation. A study of

Red-necked Grebes in Manitoba in the early 1980s revealed how the birds were suffering from the other well-known problem of a predator, namely the adverse effects of the accumulation in their bodies of persistent organochlorines, especially DDE, which is metabolized from DDT. The presence of this chemical can cause eggshells to be thinner than normal, leading to cracking and breaking during incubation. It has also been associated with lower egg production and increased mortality of embryos within the egg. These last effects are also linked to the presence in the body of another group of chemicals associated with reduced breeding success: polychlorinated biphenyls (PCBs). In addition, PCBs have been linked to alterations in the behaviour of birds, including courtship and breeding behaviour.

In the Manitoba study, the breeding success of a total of 126 pairs was measured through clutch size, hatching rate and mortality causes. Any unhatched eggs were removed for chemical analysis. The clutch size appeared to be normal, but hatching success seemed very low. Thus, of 697 eggs laid in 179 nests, only 147 hatched, a mere 21 per cent. It was immediately apparent that the grebes were suffering from high predation pressure, especially from raccoons. About half of all the eggs that failed to hatch were taken by them, or by other predators such as other birds or muskrats. Raccoons have

Chris Rose

been increasing and spreading in parts of North America and have become a major predator of wetland breeding birds. Other causes of failure included the death of one of the adults and flooding of nests. The remaining nests included some where one or more eggs was lost through breakage or where the parents deserted either eggs that did not hatch or partially hatched nests. In a sample of 191 eggs from 58 successful nests (ones where at least one egg of the clutch hatched), as many as 41 of the eggs (21.5 per cent) contained dead embryos. These were either partially developed or had died at the time of hatching. Other studies of grebes of several species have suggested it is reasonable to expect up to 95 per cent hatching success. Analysis of eggs that had failed to hatch revealed high levels of both DDE and PCBs, though, interestingly, the levels fell as the season progressed. This suggests that the birds were not ingesting the chemicals from their food on the breeding lake but had done so at some time during the preceding winter or at a spring staging post.

Red-necked Grebes spend the winter on the sea, in estuaries and sheltered bays, as well as many kilometres offshore where there are shallow banks with concentrations of fish within diving reach. In western Europe, there are regular wintering areas in the Baltic, with peak counts of 3,600 in the Kattegat between Denmark and Sweden, and 1,200 off the Polish coast. The intricate mix of islands and fjords off the central part of Norway's west coast has been estimated to hold up to 3,000 birds. These numbers may seem quite large, but are actually small in the context of the total population (*see* below). Few such winter concentrations have been noted off the coasts of North America, suggesting that the birds are more scattered there. However, one feature of the American Red-necked Grebe not observed in Europe is the concentrated daytime migrations. Grebes appear to be mainly nocturnal migrants and this is believed to be true of Red-necked Grebes when migrating over land. However, over water, and especially over the Great Lakes or along the coast, they move during the daytime.

Significant numbers of Red-necked Grebes have been counted passing observation points on the shores of some of the Great Lakes. The most impressive of these migrations takes place on Lake Superior during the period between mid-August and mid-September. Systematic counts during the autumn period revealed over 18,000 birds passing Whitefish Point near the south-east corner of the lake, on a bearing which suggested that these were birds from the Canadian breeding grounds in the prairie provinces of Manitoba, Saskatchewan and Alberta, and probably north into the Northwest Territories, heading towards the Atlantic coast for the winter. Presumably, this route is easier, if rather longer, than heading for the Pacific coast and having to cross the Rocky Mountains to get there. To the south-east of Lake Superior, the grebes have also been observed in some numbers passing over Lake Huron and Lake Ontario. The timing of the observed flights on the Great Lakes and the arrival times on the Atlantic coast suggests that some, at least, of the birds are pausing on the journey to undertake their annual moult. However, only a few thousand have been found doing this and more surveys are required.

There are very few opportunities actually to observe the migration of any grebe, as so few move in daylight. Mostly, the Red-necked Grebes passing Whitefish Point did so in very small groups. The median of three suggests perhaps that these were families. The largest flock seen was 74. Most of the birds flew very low, from skimming the surface to no more than 50m (165ft) above it. Although following the line of the lake shore, they stayed well out over the water, at least 750m (half a mile) offshore, and while the birds seemed content to fly over water during daytime, as soon as they reached the end of the lake, where St Mary's River joins Lake Superior to Lake Huron, they turned back. The distance between the lakes is only some 25–30km (15–18 miles), but they did not tackle this distance overland, not even following the river. Instead the birds would circle several times before returning to regular resting areas on Lake Superior. By

the next morning they would have gone, having continued their journey that night.

There are likely to be at least 50,000 Red-necked Grebes in North America and probably many more. Aerial surveys have suggested a minimum population of over 20,000 for Northwest Territories alone. The numbers in east Asia have been estimated to be about the same. The north-west European wintering population, presumably comprising the birds that breed in Scandinavia, central Europe and western Russia, may be as high as 150,000 with a similar number wintering in the Mediterranean and Black Seas coming from further east and south in Russia. Much smaller numbers are found in the Caspian Sea. These numbers suggest that the Red-necked Grebe is under no immediate threat, except perhaps locally. Its breeding habitat of small freshwaters is amply supplied in the northern boreal and northern temperate regions of both North America and Eurasia. It is true that wintering on the coast carries with it the risk of oil spills, for example, but the generally dispersed nature of such hazards should help to keep any resulting losses to a minimum.

GREAT CRESTED GREBE

PODICEPS CRISTATUS

— PALEARCTIC RACE *P.c.cristatus*: Widespread in temperate and southern Eurasia, with more northerly breeders moving south for winter.

— AFRICAN RACE *P.c.infuscatus*: Scattered populations in south, east and west central Africa, mainly sedentary.

— AUSTRALASIAN RACE *P.c.australis*: Australia (principally south and east) and New Zealand, mainly sedentary, but also rain-induced movements.

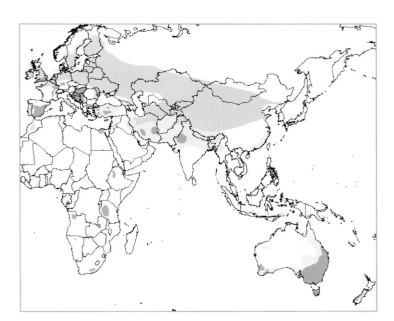

FORTUNATELY THE 20TH CENTURY SAW A REVERSAL IN the fortunes of this beautiful grebe as its numbers and range expanded through the creation of suitable man-made habitat. Things were very different in the 19th century, when large numbers of Great Crested Grebes over much of the species' European range were slaughtered to satisfy the fashion trade. The bird's fine set of head plumes – the most attractive of all the grebes – together with its thick under-pelt of soft downy feathers, were very nearly its downfall. The skin and very dense white feathers of the breast and underparts (which were known as 'grebe-fur') were made into ladies' muffs and into shoulder capes called 'tippets' – a name still given to the grebe's ear tufts. The feathers of the ear tufts and crest were often used as decoration. A large-scale traffic in pelts and feathers operated in Britain and across Europe, as furriers and milliners offered substantial rewards to shooters and trappers in country areas. The price was relatively high because the grebe was already in decline from large-scale collection of its eggs, which were regarded as a delicacy, over several decades. At the same time, there was considerable persecution by fishermen, who saw the grebe as a threat to their livelihood in places like the Norfolk Broads.

Fortunately, attitudes to birds changed quite radically in the latter part of the 19th century, which saw the formation of the Royal Society for the Protection of Birds. Its aim was to put a stop to the millinery trade in egret feathers, and to bring about the passing of a series of bird protection laws. These came only just in time in Britain, where by 1860 only some 42 pairs of Great

Crested Grebes remained. The grebe's response to protection was a rapid expansion in its range and numbers. The first full census, in 1931, found the bird widespread throughout lowland Britain, though increasingly scarce going north into Scotland, with a population of about 1,150 breeding pairs, plus a few hundreds in Ireland. The numbers continued to grow, reaching an estimated 8,000 individuals in Britain, with a further 4,500 in Ireland, by the late 1980s. This continuing increase, though interrupted from time to time by severe winters which can cause considerable mortality, has been largely brought about by man's creation of ideal grebe wetlands: fertile gravel pits in lowland areas, and a great many reservoirs. In addition, the eutrophication of these and existing wetlands, through run-off from heavily fertilized farmland, has caused substantial increases

Chris Rose

in freshwater fish and invertebrates, which form the bulk of the grebe's diet.

Similar, or even greater, increases in numbers have taken place in other European countries in recent years, for example in Finland, where the population grew from 10,000 in 1958 to 50,000–60,000 in 1983, and Sweden, which had 6,000 birds in 1971 and 10,000 by 1976. Overall, there are currently thought to be several hundred thousand in north-west Europe, and similar numbers through the Mediterranean to the Black and Caspian Seas. Further afield, the species becomes scarcer, with a few tens of thousands in south and east Asia, while the African subspecies *infuscatus* and the Australian/New Zealand subspecies *australis* each number less than 10,000 individuals, of which no more than 250 are found in New Zealand.

The display of the Great Crested Grebe has been described many times, perhaps most famously by Julian Huxley who, in 1914, published a detailed description of the courtship behaviour and used it to elaborate on Charles Darwin's suggestions about the mechanism of sexual selection in animals. Courtship begins on the water and will continue once the pair have built a nest platform. Water courtship has four principal components, usually called: head-shaking, discovery, retreat and weed ceremonies. These may occur on their own or in combination. They commence in the early spring, often among birds in a loose flock in the open water, and continue once a pair has been formed and a territory established. One bird (it seems there is no difference between the sexes) begins vocally 'advertising', using a low croaking call. It then submerges and approaches its partner, or potential partner, underwater leaving a tell-tale ripple on the surface. The partner hunches up, raising its head plumes and spreading its wings on either side of its body in a special 'cat-display' posture. The submerged bird then surfaces close beside it and immediately rears up into the 'ghostly-penguin' display, wings tight to its body and head pointing downwards. It starts with its back towards its partner and rotates slowly to

face it. This is the discovery ceremony and the pair usually move straight into head-shaking.

This is the most frequently performed ceremony, and can vary in intensity. The two birds face each other with their necks stretched up, the male's head always higher than the female's. They then wag their heads slowly from side to side, or up and down. At its most intense, the crest and plumes will be erect and the bills lowered, when a distinct 'ticking' call is given. At other times, the plumes are only slightly opened and the bills will point upwards. Head-shaking often ends with one or both birds pulling one of their long scapulars through their bill in a ritualized preening movement.

Following head-shaking, the birds may take part in the retreat ceremony, when one of the pair abruptly sets off half-flying, pattering with its feet over the water surface, before subsiding back on to the water and adopting the cat-display posture. The other bird usually stays where it is and may also go into the cat-display. If they then swim back together again, more head-shaking may ensue.

Finally, head-shaking often leads to the weed ceremony, the most spectacular of the four. As they preen their scapulars, the pair move away from each other both uttering a twanging call and both with plumes fully spread. When they are several metres apart, first one, then the other, dives slowly and deliberately and then re-emerges with a beakful of waterweed. Sometimes, one of them fails to find anything, or comes up with a stick. Approaching each other quickly, the two birds rise up vertically, breast to breast, paddling rapidly in order to maintain their position, and swing their heads, and the weed, from side to side a number of times, before subsiding on to the water, dropping the weed and indulging in a final head-shake. Seeing this display for the first time is a dramatic moment for any birdwatcher, and it is easy to see why several notable scientists have been attracted by the elaborate rituals and have sought to understand their origin and development.

Great Crested Grebes cannot mate on the water, but must do so on land, or rather on a special platform of

63

waterweed which they build for the purpose. The pair, working together, construct one or more platforms, diving for beakfuls of weed and piling it up either from the bottom, in shallow water, or on to roots and floating stems of other water plants. Once the platform can support the weight of the birds, one or other will climb on and solicit the other by lying prone and uttering the twanging call, then suddenly rearing up quivering its wings. Both of the pair do this and either may actually mount the other, but once egg-laying is imminent, proper copulation takes place.

Sometimes a mating platform is made more substantial and used as a nest, but more often a nest is specially built, placed more carefully as to anchorage and shelter. The nest is in the form of a shallow cup, with most of it below the waterline, making the inside very damp. Three to five eggs are laid at roughly two-day intervals and incubated more or less equally by the pair for about 28 days. The attractively striped young stay in the nest until the whole clutch is hatched and then, once they have left it, usually ride on their parents' backs until they are about 12 days old. The parents feed them on tiny fish and invertebrates on which they grow rapidly, being fully grown at seven to eight weeks and becoming independent about five weeks later.

Great Crested Grebes obtain all their food by diving. The average dive lasts 30 seconds, to a depth of 2–4m (6–13ft), though much greater depths are possible, down to 30m (100ft). Fish of a great variety of species, usually about 10–15cm (4–6in) long, form the main part of the diet, though these grebes also eat many different invertebrates, including larvae of beetles and dragonflies, crayfish and molluscs, as well as tadpoles.

The nominate subspecies is very widespread across most of temperate and southern Europe and Asia, and has a population estimated at not less than 300,000. The other two subspecies are much more restricted in their ranges and have much smaller populations. The African subspecies has a patchy distribution with more or less isolated small populations thought to number only a few thousand in Ethiopia, Kenya, Tanzania, Cameroon, Namibia and South Africa. The birds are found mostly on lakes in the cooler uplands, and are slightly smaller and darker than the nominate form of Eurasia. So, too, is the Australian subspecies, which is found in the extreme south-west of Western Australia, and from Queensland to Victoria, South Australia and Tasmania. Estimates of up to 10,000 have been made, but the true total may be only half that. In 1988, there were records of 250 birds from 32 different lakes in South Island, New Zealand, but the bird occurs on North Island only as a vagrant. Neither subspecies appears to have a distinct non-breeding plumage, unlike the nominate form which loses all its attractive finery during the winter months.

Horned Grebe

Podiceps auritus

— Also known (for example in Britain) as Slavonian Grebe.

— PALEARCTIC RACE *P.a.auritus*: Breeds northern temperate Palearctic from Iceland to Kamchatka, wintering in coasts of western Europe, Mediterranean and coast of east Asia.

— NORTH AMERICA RACE *P.a.cornutus*: Breeds in Alaska and western Canada and extreme north-west United States, winters Pacific coast from Alaska to Baja California and Atlantic coast from Nova Scotia to Gulf of Mexico, and inland in south-eastern United States from Florida to Texas.

IT HAS BEEN SUGGESTED THAT THE BIRDS BREEDING IN Iceland, Britain and Norway were larger-billed than those breeding from the Baltic eastwards and that they should be placed in a separate subspecies, but this proposal has not been widely accepted.

Although most familiar to birdwatchers in its essentially black and white non-breeding plumage, the Horned (or Slavonian) Grebe has one of the most attractive breeding plumages in the grebe family. Golden ear-tufts run back from the bright red eye and are framed by a black cap to the head and black tippets (side plumes), above a reddish-chestnut neck and breast. The ear-tufts are held erect during displays, giving the bird the appearance of wearing a pair of horns, hence its North American name. Its alternative name, used only in Britain, comes from a remark in an early 19th-century book on birds which called it the 'Sclavonian Grebe' after the old name of Sclavonia for the area of northern Russia where it had been found breeding. The spelling was changed to 'Slavonian' by later 19th-century authors.

The displays of the Horned Grebe are as varied and spectacular as those of the other grebes, perhaps more so because the birds enhance their appearance with raised golden ear tufts contrasting with their black tippets. Displays between pairs include an advertising ceremony accompanied by a harsh trill and a triumph ceremony when both birds utter a more rapid, musical, trill. Their weed ceremony differs from that of all other grebes. It starts normally, with each bird diving and bringing up pieces of waterweed and approaching the other, but instead of the weed being dropped in front of or over the back of the mate as in other species, the pair rise up in the water breast to breast then, still holding the weed,

turn parallel to each other and, holding their upright position, rush across the water for up to 10m (33ft), before subsiding and moving apart. However, it does not end there, as the pair immediately come together again and perform another rush in a different direction. They may repeat the performance up to 15 times.

The Horned Grebe breeds in most north-western and northern European countries, though it is nowhere very common, with a total of between 5,000 and 10,000 pairs outside Russia. It has been monitored fairly effectively in several countries, sufficient to record changes in status in recent years. The most important country is Finland, where the most recent figures suggest a population of between 3,000 and 6,000 breeding pairs – similar to the first estimates made in 1950. However, there was a sharp decline in the 1970s followed by a recovery in the late 1980s and 1990s. The reasons for these changes are not clear. The next most important countries are Finland's neighbours Sweden (1,000–2,000 pairs) and Norway (500–1,000 pairs). In Sweden there were substantial increases in the first half of the 20th century but this has since been followed by a decline in many areas. Increases have taken place in parts of Norway, where the range has expanded south so that the population may have doubled in the last 40 years. Conversely, both Iceland and Estonia, with about 300 pairs

Chris Ruse

each, have seen recent declines, in the case of Iceland from over 500 pairs not many years ago. The only other countries with breeding birds are Latvia (200–300 pairs), Britain (60 pairs, all in Scotland) and less than 10 pairs each in Belarus, Lithuania and Moldova. It is hard to explain all the changes in numbers of breeding Horned Grebes in different European countries because there is no single common trend. It has been suggested that decreases can be blamed on increasing acidification of the small freshwaters where the birds like to breed, destroying the abundant plant and insect life on which they depend. On the other hand, increases have been attributed to eutrophication arising from agricultural run-off, giving a short-term boost to both vegetation and food, though a reduction may follow if algal blooms occur in the enriched water.

Some insight into the problems with the breeding waters of Horned Grebes can be gained by looking at the small Scottish population. This has been in existence for less than a century: the first pair bred near Inverness in 1908, at a time when a general expansion appeared to be taking place in Europe. Colonization was slow and it was not until the late 1920s that two new breeding areas were established in Caithness and in Sutherland, to the north-east and north of Inverness respectively. However, these areas became deserted by the 1970s and, apart from scattered short-term nesting in a few other areas, the present population is still centred around the original area, having spread out from it by no more than 65km (40 miles). In the early 1970s, the population was around 40 pairs but increasing steadily so that by the late 1970s and early 1980s the total was about 80 pairs. Since then, however, there has been a considerable decline, halted briefly in the early 1990s, when numbers, which had fallen to about 60, rose to just over 70 again. However, in the last ten years the breeding total has plunged to no more than 31 pairs in 2000. This decline has been accompanied by an equally drastic drop in the number of occupied waters, from 34 in 1992, when there were 72 pairs, to

only 15 in 2000. Productivity, too, has been declining through the 1990s, though it leaped up again in 2000 to a record figure.

Just one water in Scotland – Loch Ruthven, south of Inverness – has long been of great importance to the Horned Grebe. In fact, its importance has increased in the last ten years as the number of breeding pairs there has been maintained despite the decline and disappearance from so many lochs elsewhere. It is one of the larger breeding waters, at about 3.2km (2 miles) long by about 300m (330yd) wide. In 1992, 16 pairs bred there out of 72, whereas in 2000 the figure was 14 pairs out of 31. The loch has been a reserve of the Royal Society for the Protection of Birds since the 1980s. One of the original aims of the reserve was to provide viewing facilities for birdwatchers in order to take the pressure off other sites, where disturbance was known to be a problem. In the last two years, some habitat management has been carried out to try and increase the available emergent vegetation in which the grebes breed. A shortage of suitable nesting habitat had been identified as one potential factor preventing any increase in the number of pairs breeding on the loch. Clumps of suitable sedges were moved into areas of shallow water close to the bank, but establishment of the plants has been slow and it is too soon to know whether it will be successful.

Looking in detail at all the lochs used for breeding in Scotland, it is clear that Horned Grebes, while using some year after year without fail, also breed casually on different waters in different years, sometimes just once, sometimes returning irregularly over a period. Thus through the 1970s and 1980s, a total of 74 different lochs was used for breeding, though the greatest number used in any one year was 34 and the lowest only 17. For some lochs, it was possible to identify a reason why breeding had stopped, for example, afforestation of the surrounding land, or the building of houses close to the shore. However, examination of such factors as water quality, fish populations and the presence of at least some emergent vegetation has failed to find any obvious

changes that would cause the grebes to give up breeding on a particular loch. There may be some more subtle changes at work. If so, these may affect productivity, which fell during the 1990s. This in turn is likely to reduce the number of adults in future years.

In North America, degrading of breeding waters through agricultural run-off has been detected in some areas. Overall, the total North American population of around 100,000 appears to be in slow decline, and the breeding range has become smaller in some areas. The reasons for this are unclear, though it is recognized that the grebe is especially vulnerable to oiling incidents in its coastal winter quarters, where it occupies lagoons and estuaries. An oil spill in Chesapeake Bay in 1976 killed more than 4,000 grebes. The Western European population of perhaps 25,000–50,000 birds may be even more vulnerable to oiling because it is relatively concentrated in winter, for example, 1,700 birds were found in the southern Baltic off the Polish coast. Further east, it is believed that between 10,000 and 25,000 of the birds winter in the Black and Caspian Seas and even larger numbers in eastern Asia.

68

BLACK-NECKED GREBE

PODICEPS NIGRICOLLIS

— Also known (for example in North America) as Eared Grebe.
— EURASIAN RACE *P.n.nigricollis*: Western Europe east to western Asia, wintering to west and south; central-east Asia; eastern Africa.
— SOUTH AFRICAN RACE *P.n.gurneyi*: Southern Africa.
— NORTH AMERICAN RACE *P.n.californicus*: South-western Canada, western United States, west and central Mexico, wintering south to Guatemala.
— Races separated on slight differences in plumage coloration.

THE HEADLINE IN THE *MONO LAKE NEWSLETTER* FOR spring 2000 reads: '1.6 million grebes and counting'. The article reports on regular autumn aerial surveys over the previous four years which have found between 800,000 and 1.6 million grebes, every single one of them Black-necked. Even higher figures are thought actually to be present, because observations have shown that, at any one moment, between 15 and 20 per cent of the birds are feeding underwater. Thus the total is probably between 1 and 2 million – a very large proportion of the total population of the species in North America, which peaks after the breeding season at about 4 million. Considering the huge importance of Mono Lake to the Black-necked Grebe and a number of other waterbirds, it seems amazing that the lake was well on its way to being destroyed as a bird-rich wetland, and saved only after legal battles that went all the way to the State of California Supreme Court.

Mono Lake is a large, more or less circular water with an area of about 184sq km (71sq miles). It lies at 1,945m (6,384ft) above sea level in the Sierra Nevada range some 300km (185 miles) due east of San Francisco. The water is saline, through evaporation, and holds vast quantities of algae, brine shrimps and specialized insects. These attract large numbers of birds, both to breed and to stage on their migration. In another part of the world, one would expect to see flamingos on such a wetland. In 1941, well before any detailed studies had been made of the wildlife riches of Mono Lake, the Los Angeles Water and Power Board diverted four of the five

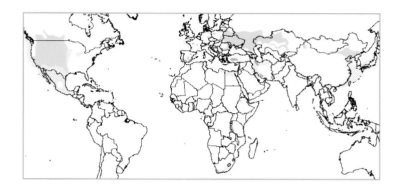

streams flowing into Mono Lake in order to use their pure water to supply the fast-growing city. The effects of this action took some time to appear, but by the late 1970s, when local conservationists began to notice, they had already proved very damaging and were set to be catastrophic. In the period between 1941 and 1982, the lack of inflowing water caused the level of the lake to drop by more than 13.5m (45ft), shrinking the surface area by one-third and the volume by more than one-half, while at the same time the salinity doubled. The brine shrimps began to decline, once-important brackish lagoons around the edge of the lake dried out, marshland vegetation disappeared and cottonwood forests in the floodplains of the inlet streams died. Had nothing been done to stop this process, it was calculated that in another 40 years the salinity would have nearly doubled again and the lake would have become a wildlife desert.

Fortunately, something was done, and just in time. The Mono Lake Committee was formed in 1978 and since then has reversed the situation, after a long battle

through the courts, by persuading the California Water Resources Control Board to pass an ordnance in 1994 drastically reducing the amount of water permitted to be diverted. This has been linked to a restoration plan to allow the lake level to rise by about 6m (20ft) from its lowest point, which will also increase the surface area to about 87 per cent of its original size. It is estimated that it will take about 15–20 years to achieve this compromise solution, depending on rainfall. A succession of wet or dry years would speed up or slow down the rate of recovery. Because the final level will still be below the level required for restoration of some of the former marginal lagoons and marshland, habitat creation has been included in the programme.

The first Black-necked Grebes arrive on Mono Lake in late July and early August and birds continue to arrive throughout September and into October. The vast hordes of grebes feed almost exclusively on the brine shrimps and during the course of their stay may double or even treble their body weight. They start from a mean of 260g (9oz) and attain a mean peak of 600g (21oz), with a maximum of 735g (26oz). This enormous gain in mass has been described as being so great as to prevent them from flying, which is strictly true, although what is occurring is both more complicated, and more extraordinary, than simple obesity. The grebes actually go through a remarkable series of physiological changes which enable them to benefit to the utmost from the superabundance of food in the lake. In the weeks after arrival, as the birds feed as much as they can, their pectoral muscles, which power their wings, shrink by about 50 per cent. This means they are well below the size needed for flight, and the birds become flightless. They are also moulting their wing feathers at this time, so they do not need their wings. With the wing muscles reduced in size and the birds able to catch as much food as they can eat, the next change is to the digestive organs, the stomach and the intestines, which double in size and weight. This is not all: the leg muscles and the heart both also increase in size, as aids to the birds' continuous diving. Finally, the

liver, a key storage organ, enlarges and the birds also lay down considerable masses of fat.

After a few weeks on Mono Lake, the Black-necked Grebes are twice or even three times their arrival weight and have become flightless. However, they are on a mountain lake which is unsuitable for spending the coming winter. Although even 1–2 million grebes cannot eat all the estimated 2–4 trillion brine shrimps in the lake, the shrimps die off as winter arrives, so the grebes must leave. In order to do this they have to reverse the physiological changes they have undergone, reducing their overall weight and restoring the size and power of their wing muscles. The shrimps disappear quite quickly, triggering the changes in the grebes, which have to stop feeding and so start losing weight. After a two- to three-week period of fasting, their average body weight is about 450g (16oz). At the same time, they are able to divert some of their stored fat to their wing muscles, which double in weight, while the digestive organs and leg muscles correspondingly shrink. The changes which took place gradually over two or three months are undone in a matter of two or three weeks and the birds depart on migration.

These major physiological changes are not confined to the autumn staging period, they also take place on the wintering grounds further south and in spring, indeed whenever the birds stop for a prolonged period in one place. Thus, breeding adults will undergo probably three of these cycles, while immature birds, which do not breed until their second year, may achieve up to six cycles. During each one, the same changes take place, though those in winter and spring may not be so marked as in the autumn. Because the grebes go flightless each time through pectoral muscle atrophy, the total period of flightlessness is longer than for any other known flying bird. Adults on the autumn staging lakes, like Lake Mono, may be flightless for three or four months at a time, while for any immatures which have returned to the lake and stayed there throughout the summer the period can exceed eight months. It is thought that some immatures

71

may be flightless for nine or ten months in the course of their second calendar year – an astonishing total.

The concentration of perhaps half the total North American population of Black-necked Grebes on the single site of Lake Mono, with another 400,000 on the Great Salt Lake in Utah, about 600km (375 miles) to the north-east, is unique to this population. There are an estimated half a million Black-necked Grebes in Europe and western Asia, but no such staging posts have been found and consequently the grebes are not known to go through this dramatic cycle of physiological change. Elsewhere, the grebe is very much scarcer, with perhaps 50,000 in eastern Asia and a few tens of thousands in southern Africa. Other species of grebe and waterbird also become flightless through shedding all their wing feathers at once, but they do not simultaneously, and significantly, reduce the muscles, too.

The dependence of the North American population of Black-necked Grebes on a handful of autumn staging locations gives obvious cause for concern, especially when, as the water extraction at Mono Lake showed, it is possible for drastic changes to occur to the lake ecology in a matter of a few decades. Fortunately, in that instance, the situation has been at least partially reversed, but worrying signs of declining shrimp populations at Great Salt Lake suggest that its ecosystem is also in trouble. The Black-necked Grebe faces problems at other haunts, too. An estimated 150,000 grebes on the Salton Sea in southern California died in 1991, possibly from avian cholera. The grebe's habit of migrating at night has also led to major incidents when thousands of birds, attracted to lights in fog or snow, have come crashing to the ground. About 35,000 birds were estimated to have been grounded in this way in one short winter period in the 1990s. They were part of a large-scale migration south from Great Salt Lake, and ran into adverse weather. Despite these occurrences, the population remains abundant and not under threat. There is insufficient evidence to know whether populations elsewhere in the world are equally secure, though Black-necked Grebes were one of the commonest species among the estimated 100,000 birds killed by oil spills in the Persian Gulf during the 1991 war.

GREBES OF THE WORLD

COLOMBIAN GREBE

PODICEPS ANDINUS

— Formerly on lakes in the Andes of northern central Colombia.

THE COLOMBIAN GREBE IS THOUGHT TO HAVE BECOME extinct in the 1960s, though a few birds may have survived into the 1970s. Unlike another extinct species, the Atitlán Grebe, no-one fought for it or raised international awareness to the point where conservation measures could be introduced. But then this grebe was confined to Colombia, often a politically unsettled country, and most of the agricultural development in the area where it lived occurred well before any conservationist became aware of the drastic decline of the grebe. These factors effectively prevented any major measures being taken.

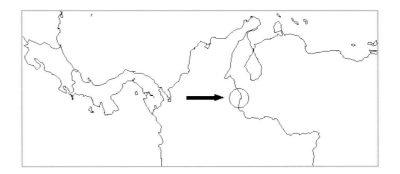

The Colombian Grebe is often considered to have been a subspecies of the Black-necked Grebe, which it certainly resembles, though it had more chestnut on the head tufts and had a chestnut (not black) foreneck and upper breast. However when it was first described, as recently as 1945, it was treated as a full species. It lived in the High Andes north of Bogotá, the capital of Colombia, in the departments of Boyacá and Cundinmarca. The plateaux of Bogotá and Ubate formerly held many lakes and marshes, but a large-scale drainage programme begun in the 1940s converted many of them to agricultural land complete with areas of greenhouses and plantations of eucalyptus. Those wetlands that survived became very polluted through run-off of fertilizer and pesticides, and much wildlife disappeared as a result.

The principal known haunt of the Colombian Grebe, and the one where it survived the longest, was Lake Tota, lying at 3,015m (nearly 10,000ft) above sea level. The lake extends to about 56sq km (215sq miles) and formerly had an extensive growth of alder scrub and tall reed-beds around its margins, together with large areas of submerged aquatic vegetation in the shallows, especially pond-weeds *Potamogeton*. In the 1950s the water level was deliberately reduced by about 1m (3ft) in order to increase the amount of agricultural land. This, combined with eutrophication caused by fertilizer run-off,

drastically reduced this marginal vegetation and also led to huge beds of Canadian pond-weed *Elodea* replacing the *Potamogeton*, where the grebes did most of their feeding.

Elodea grows too densely for grebes to forage readily, unlike *Potamogeton*, which is more open and allows the grebes to feed both on the surface, snapping up invertebrates from among the leaves, and to dive between the leaves and stems for underwater prey. Another adverse effect on the grebes of Lake Tota came earlier with the introduction, in 1944, of rainbow trout, which are thought to have greatly reduced the available invertebrates and even preyed on grebe chicks.

In the 1940s, the grebe was regarded as 'abundant' on Lake Tota, though there are no actual counts. It also occurred regularly on other lakes in the region. By the 1960s, however, many of these other haunts had been drained and the remaining ones were no longer suitable, while Lake Tota was already badly degraded. In addition, it is known that hunting took place on the lake, including during the breeding season, and this probably played a part in the final extinction of this already vulnerable species. Local hunters reported that the grebes were very easy to shoot when they were nesting. When disturbed, instead of skulking among the vegetation they swam out into the open water nearest to their nest, making them easy targets. Whole colonies are believed to have been wiped out in this way in the mid-1960s.

There is a record of 300 Colombian Grebes on Lake Tota in 1968, and there were also sightings of one bird in 1972 and of 'one, and possibly two more' in February 1977. Searches made here, and elsewhere in the Colombian highlands, in 1981 and 1982 failed to find any. There is some doubt as to whether the 300 seen in 1968 were, in fact, Colombian Grebes, and the same has been said about the isolated sightings in 1972 and 1977. Whether or not these were in fact Colombian Grebes, it is probably reasonable to assume that the species had declined beyond the point of no return by the end of the 1960s and disappeared for good in the 1970s.

The habits of the Colombian Grebe were never studied, though it can be assumed that its feeding and breeding behaviour were very similar to the Black-necked Grebe, as might be expected from such a closely related species. They fed mainly from the surface of the water, taking a variety of aquatic invertebrates, including small snails and crustaceans, as well as insect larvae. When they dived, they did so to pick items off stems and leaves of vegetation rather than to indulge in underwater pursuit of fish.

It is known that the grebes bred in colonies and that the principal breeding season was from August to about October. Nothing seems to have been recorded relating to clutch size or incubation or fledging periods, though they are unlikely to have differed much from those of the Black-necked Grebe. There are a few anecdotes relating to their courtship displays and such accounts as there are appear to indicate that they were not as elaborate as those of other species. If this was actually the case, then it would have reinforced the decision to classify the Colombian Grebe as a separate species rather than, as some still maintain, merely a subspecies of the Black-necked Grebe. Sadly, this issue is unlikely to ever be resolved.

GREBES OF THE WORLD

SILVERY GREBE

PODICEPS OCCIPITALIS

— SOUTHERN RACE *P.o.occipitalis*: Central and southern Chile and Argentina south to Tierra del Fuego, and Falkland Islands.
— NORTHERN RACE *P.o.juninensis*: From Colombia south to northern Chile and north-western Argentina.

THIS SMALL AND DAINTY GREBE IS VERY WELL NAMED, with a white neck, breast and underparts, greyish flanks and black down the hindneck and on the back. The head is black and decorated with plumes (grey and yellow in the southern race, just grey in the northern) which are absent during the winter. The northern race looks like a smaller version of the Junín Flightless Grebe, though the proportions are also different as the neck and bill are both much shorter. Both species occur on Lake Junín but have never, as far as is known, hybridized.

The southern race of the Silvery Grebe has been estimated to number around 100,000 individuals. Flocks numbering between 1,000 and 2,000 have been seen on various wetlands in Chile and Argentina, though there has been nothing recent to match the 10,000 birds which Alexander Wetmore saw in the 1920s from just one place on the shores of Lake Epecuen about 600km (375 miles) south-west of Buenos Aires. The lake is large (160sq km, 62sq miles), shallow and saline, formed as it was on the site of former salt-mining. It may have increased in size through subsidence and flooding since Wetmore's day, but even so his count must have represented only a proportion of the birds that were present. There are good numbers of birds breeding on the lakes of the Andes in Chile and Argentina, up to altitudes of around 2,800m (9,000ft), but the majority of this race occurs no higher than 1,200m (4,000ft) and also comes down to the lowlands. It also breeds at sea level in the Falklands, where it is locally common with around 500 breeding pairs.

The northern race occupies much higher ground than the southern race, extending to as high as 5,000m (16,000ft). It is sometimes termed the Andean race in recognition of this. There is no available population estimate. Although it has been described as abundant in Peru and Bolivia, there are signs of decline further

north, in Ecuador and Colombia, following drainage of wetlands and loss of water-weed through eutrophication, an increase in nutrients in the water from agricultural run-off. Conversely, the fairly recent colonization of lakes in central Colombia suggests that the range is expanding northwards at least in that country.

The Silvery Grebe is a very gregarious species, both during the breeding season and in winter. A single colony in Tierra del Fuego was estimated to contain over 1,000 pairs and others totalling hundreds have been recorded. Within the colonies, the nests are not evenly distributed, but distinctly clustered, perhaps in relation to the distribution of the aquatic vegetation. Some nests are built on floating vegetation out in the open with minimal cover, while others are placed in the centre of a dense clump of vegetation. In these latter cases, the nests are usually in areas where the clumps themselves are not too dense, so that the birds have ready access to open water, both for

swimming and for diving. The Danish ornithologist, Jon Fjeldså, who has been responsible for discovering far more about South American grebes than anyone else, observed one colony in Peru of 62 nests in an area of water-weed about 100 × 80m (330 × 260ft). These nests were grouped into four main clusters of between 8 and 23. Within these were clumps of nests, some of which, for example seven within an area of no more than 1sq m (10.7sq ft), were actually touching.

Aggression between such closely nesting birds was almost nil. Indeed, the Silvery Grebe seems more peaceable than some other grebes, though fights can occur during courtship, perhaps especially when another grebe interferes with a pair during copulation. The range of courtship displays parallels those in its closest relatives: in South America, the Hooded Grebe and the Junín Flightless Grebe; and, in the northern hemisphere and in South Africa, the Black-necked Grebe. However, one display is more pronounced in the Silvery Grebe than in the others. This involves the adults collecting pieces of water-weed, either by diving or picking it up from the surface, and approaching each other with their crests raised and necks held straight up. In other grebes, collecting weed like this is usually the first move in a weed-dance or when the pair rushes across the water together. In the Silvery Grebe, although pairs do sometimes indulge in short rushes while holding the weed, more often it is presented by one bird to the other, by either dropping it on the water in front of the other bird or, with a flick of the head, throwing it across the other bird's breast or back. The latter does not always appear to be welcomed by the bird on the receiving end, which may turn away to avoid the weed. The whole behaviour sequence is a bit of a puzzle because it usually takes place in open water, so cannot really be regarded as some preliminary to nest-building. However, when nest-building does start, both birds of the pair may collect weed and swim with it together to the nest site, so perhaps there is some connection after all.

Silvery Grebes are comparatively poor divers compared with most other species. They make mostly shorter dives with longer pauses in between. This probably explains their requirement for open water around their nests. It may also explain why it has been observed that they tend to dive more in open water than in among dense beds of water-weed, in which other grebes will happily feed. In fact, the bulk of their feeding is not by diving at all, but is carried out on the surface by pecking invertebrates from among the floating leaves of water plants and catching small flying insects on the wing. Midges form an important part of the diet in the breeding season. During major hatches, the grebes can be seen pecking vigorously at the surface and reaching up to catch the midges in flight. They move rapidly to and fro, even making short rushes half out of the water to seize their prey. Pecking rates of 40–50 a minute have been observed, and once over 90. Small wonder, then, that an examination of the stomach contents of some birds revealed many hundreds of midges.

The birds breeding in the extreme south of the range, in Tierra del Fuego and the southernmost parts of Argentina, are migratory, disappearing to the north for the winter, though it is not known how far they travel. During the winter, large flocks turn up on large lowland lakes in Argentina, including saline ones, as mentioned above. Here the Silvery Grebes may share the wetlands, and the invertebrates they contain, with flocks of flamingos. They are virtually unknown on the South American coasts, but in the Falklands, numbers of birds do spend the winter feeding in the numerous bays and inlets where they are protected by the extensive kelp beds.

Although the northern race may be experiencing some problems in the north of its range as wetlands disappear or become less suitable, overall the Silvery Grebe is not threatened other than locally, though it would be helpful if more of its main wintering haunts could be identified and then periodic censuses carried out.

Junín Flightless Grebe

Podiceps taczanowskii

— Originally confined to Lake Junín, Peru, but recently introduced to other, neighbouring, lakes.

The Junín Flightless Grebe is just hanging on, though badly threatened by a combination of mining pollution and artificial fluctuations of the water-level. Its sole haunt is Lake Junín, which lies at 4,080m (13,385ft) above sea level in the Peruvian Andes. The lake, the second largest in Peru, is about 530sq km (about 200sq miles) in extent, but is very shallow, no more than 12.5m (41ft) at its deepest point. The Junín Flightless Grebe is closely related to the Silvery Grebe and it is believed that a population of these became isolated on the lake several tens of thousands of years ago, probably during a period of glaciation, and gradually went flightless as the need to fly to escape predators or find food became redundant.

The Junín Flightless Grebe is larger than the Silvery Grebe and has a longer neck. It is very similar in plumage to the northern race of that species, with greyish head plumes (not the yellowish ones of the southern race). The Silvery Grebe is also present at Lake Junín. However, the two birds do not hybridize, which tends to confirm that they have been separated a long time in evolutionary terms. The Junín Flightless Grebes breed colonially in the vast reed-beds, which are up to 6km (3.7 miles) wide in places, while outside the breeding season they live in small flocks of a dozen or so feeding among equally vast beds of stonecrops *Chara*. The birds indulge in communal feeding, swimming in line abreast and then diving simultaneously, a behaviour which probably increases the chances of catching fish by causing a shoal to bunch or for them to be disturbed by one bird into the path of another. Small fish, under 2.5cm (1in) long, form the bulk of their diet, supplemented by invertebrates.

Breeding colonies have been found containing up to 20 pairs, nesting 1–4m (3–13ft) apart. As with other grebes, the young are carried on their parents' backs, although in the rather few observations for this species only the adult males were seen carrying the young. As the normal clutch and brood is only two, there is clearly less need for both parents to share this duty, even though flightless grebes have much less room among the wing feathers for the chicks to tuck themselves into.

The grebe was first described in 1894 and was named in honour of Dr Wladyslaw Taczanowski, the late Conservator of the Zoological Cabinet (later the Museum) in Warsaw. The Cabinet had sent out expeditions to South America in the 1870s and 1880s and Dr Taczanowski wrote a three-volume work on the birds of Peru, published in 1884–1886 and based on the collections and data brought back. The work is still regarded as important today. The two people who named the grebe after Dr Taczanowski were Count Hans von Berlepsch and Jean Stolzmann (Jan Sztolcman in Polish). Von Berlepsch sponsored much collecting work in South America, specializing in hummingbirds, and also wrote many important papers on avian systematics. Stolzmann was a member of the Warsaw Zoological Cabinet expeditions to Peru and succeeded Dr Taczanowski as Conservator.

In the years following its discovery, the Junín Flightless Grebe was generally described as abundant, for example in 1938, and may have numbered several thousand as the studies have indicated that the lake could support a population of this size. Ornithologists visiting Lake Junín in 1961 found the grebe to be common and estimated that there were well over 1,000 of them, although they did not carry out a full census. However, not long after this, the

Chris Rose

population slumped, though a report in 1968 that it had become extinct was, happily, mistaken. Sample counts in 1977 and 1978 suggested a population of around 100 pairs, with a total of about 300 individuals.

The reasons for this dramatic decrease are twofold. Since the 1930s, mining for lead, zinc and copper has taken place close to the San Juan river, which flows into the lake at its north end bringing with it toxic waste from the mines. Levels in the lake of all these heavy metals are very high and a threat to the fish and invertebrates. Iron oxides have been building up in the lake mud, colouring whole areas red. The situation in the lake has become worse since 1955 when a hydro-electric dam was built across the main outlet river from the lake to provide power for the mines. The resultant fluctuations in water level have had a drastic effect on the vegetation, both emergent and submerged.

During drought periods, the water level may drop several metres, not only drying out the reed-beds but also concentrating the mining pollutants and killing birds, fish and invertebrates. Conversely, when the rains come, and particularly when rainfall is above average, the resulting floods discolour the normally crystal-clear lake water so heavily with iron-oxide that it becomes murky. This prevents the grebes from finding their prey under-water, while the sediment chokes the submerged vegetation on which so much of the aquatic life depends. In 1993 and 1994, heavy rains caused flooding of the meadows around the shore of the lake, covering them in a grey deposit which was so toxic that it caused the death of perhaps 2,000 cattle which grazed there.

In the last 20 years, the population has been estimated a number of times, mainly by doing boat transects along the borders of the reed-beds. Nearly all the totals have been between 200 and 300 birds, with the exception of 1992 when no more than 100 could be found. This followed what appears to have been a total breeding failure after two or three years of extreme drought during which there was mass mortality of fish and waterbirds, though whether this included grebes is not known. In recent years, small numbers of grebes have been caught and released on neighbouring lakes in an attempt both to increase the total population and reduce its dependence on a single wetland. However, the capacity of most lakes close to Lake Junín is probably no more than about 40 pairs.

A species recovery plan for the Junín Flightless Grebe, written for the International Union for the Conservation of Nature in 1997, not only proposed the continuing release of birds on other waters, but also stressed the urgent need to persuade the mining companies to manage both the water levels of the lake and the run-off from their activities in such a way as to reduce the disastrous effect both have had on the lake and all its wildlife, not just the grebe. The mines in one area installed waste purification plants in 1978, but others have not yet been persuaded that they should do so.

Also in 1997, the Peruvian government declared Lake Junín a Ramsar site – one of a number of wetlands deemed important enough for designation under the Ramsar International Convention on the Conservation of Wetlands and Waterfowl. At the least, this commits the Peruvian authorities to ensuring the wetland and its birds are protected. It also helps draw attention to the need to take positive steps towards saving the wetland from further damage and, in the long term, restoring it to its former state. Unfortunately, little or no money is available for even the basic study of the grebes and other birds, let alone the major works needed to restore the habitat.

One positive factor in recent years has been the increasing number of bird enthusiasts who come to see the Junín Flightless Grebe and another very rare endemic, the Junín Rail. Several tour companies now include the lake on their itineraries, hiring boats to take birdwatchers out on the lake to increase the chances of seeing the grebe. Elsewhere in the world, ecotourism has already been shown to give a considerable stimulus to the local economy. It also helps to demonstrate to the relevant authorities the international importance of what they are trying to look after. There is a long way to go before the Junín Flightless Grebe can be considered safe from extinction, but at least the first steps are being taken.

HOODED GREBE

PODICEPS GALLARDOI

— Occurs on a small number of lakes in the uplands of extreme southern Argentina and Chile.

THE HOODED GREBE WAS DISCOVERED MORE OR LESS BY accident in 1974 when two naturalists, Maurice Rumboll and Edward Shaw, visited Laguna de Los Escarchados. This lake, which is about 3km (2 miles) long, lies at about 700m (2,300ft) above sea level in the eastern foothills of the Andes in the extreme south-west of Argentina. In order to teach Shaw how to prepare a study skin, Rumboll shot a grebe on the lake. Both White-tufted and Silvery Grebes were present, but it was not until the specimen was later examined in the National Museum of Natural History in Buenos Aires that it was discovered that it was not a Silvery Grebe, as first thought, but a species new to science.

The year after the Hooded Grebe's discovery, the distinguished ornithologist and expert on grebes, Professor Robert Storer, then Curator of Birds at the Museum of Zoology in the University of Michigan, travelled to the lake, with Maurice Rumboll and two companions, to carry out the first study of its ecology and behaviour and also to make the first estimates of population size. The highest count they made was of 126 birds, in late December. Numbers fell over the next three weeks as the birds left for their winter quarters which, at that time, were a mystery. Professor Storer also carried out an aerial survey of neighbouring lakes but, although some looked suitable, no more grebes were found so this was assumed to be a very rare endemic, perhaps occurring only on this one lake.

In 1978, Hooded Grebes were found breeding in very small numbers on two lakes quite close to Laguna de Los Escarchados, but the total population was still thought to be no more than 150. The Laguna was declared a nature reserve the following year, but then, in 1981, it was found that the population of grebes had slumped to no more than 75. The main cause was breeding failures, apparently through heavy predation of eggs and small chicks by Kelp Gulls, which were common there. However, while this information was being digested, news came of the discovery of a second colony of Hooded Grebes on another lake,

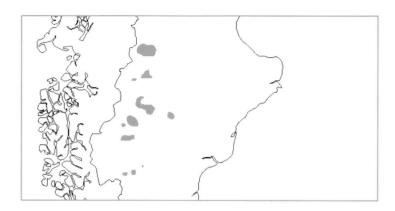

this time on the Meseta de Tobiano, a plateau some 120km (75 miles) to the north. About 250 birds were counted here, quadrupling the known world population. Alarmingly, though, these birds, too, were suffering very severe predation by Kelp Gulls so that, only three years later, just 45 individuals could be found.

It seemed that, a mere ten years after its discovery, the Hooded Grebe was destined for extinction, despite frantic efforts by local conservationists involving controlling the gulls and other predators, undertaking the artificial incubation of the eggs and embarking on a captive breeding programme. Then, in the same year, the pressure was relieved with the discovery on the Meseta de Strobel, further to the north, of some 1,500 pairs. They are spread across the hundreds of small lakes scattered throughout the 1,200sq km (460sq miles) of this remote region lying at an altitude of 800–1,200m (2,600–3,900ft) between the much larger Lakes Cardiel and Strobel. The total population is now believed to number up to 5,000 birds and the threats that exist at the original haunts do not appear to be a problem in what is now recognized as the core of the range. Indeed, it may well be that the small populations at Laguna de Los Escarchados and on the Meseta de Tobiano are merely suffering the kind of fluctuations and irregular breeding to be expected of locations at the edge of a range.

Unlike nearly all other grebes, the Hooded Grebe does not breed in dense stands of vegetation for the

simple reason that the windswept lakes it inhabits are so exposed that little or no vegetation grows above water. Instead the nest is built of, and attached to, the thick floating mats of water-milfoil *Myriophyllum* that form the dominant aquatic plant growth of almost all the lakes. The nest platform is also larger than that of most other grebes, presumably a further adaptation to the inevitable wave action produced by the incessant wind. Professor Storer reported gusts of over 100kph (over 60mph) at Laguna de Los Escarchados in the middle of the austral summer. Not only are the nests in full view, but the Hooded Grebe is one of the most conspicuous of all the grebes. Apart from its black head, with its white and chestnut plumes, a thin black stripe down the back of the neck and black in the centre of its back, the rest of the bird, including its neck, breast, underparts, flanks and wings, is pure white. Thus the incubating bird stands out clearly at a considerable distance, seeming to shine in the sunlight. It is perhaps for this reason that the grebes nest in colonies, sometimes of as many as 75 pairs, as a defence against predators.

Hooded Grebes have a very low rate of reproduction and recruitment, each breeding pair managing, on average, to rear only one young every second or third year. They never lay more than two eggs and have never been known to rear more than one young. The eggs are laid at intervals of, probably, two days and incubation starts with the first egg so that hatching is also asynchronous. If the first egg hatches successfully, both parents take that young on to the water and abandon the other egg. Even having hatched one chick, the parents are quite capable of abandoning it after a few days if there is insufficient food in the breeding lake. This is very unusual behaviour. All other grebes, indeed virtually all other birds whose eggs hatch over a period of days, continue with incubation until the complete clutch has hatched.

One feature of all the smaller breeding lakes is the complete absence of fish. Hooded Grebes feed instead on a mixture of invertebrates, especially snails, shrimps, and the larvae and pupae of a variety of aquatic species. As well as diving for this food among the submerged beds of water-milfoil, the grebes feed on the surface, snatching items from the floating leaves. Some of the breeding lakes are quite small and contain limited supplies of invertebrates on which the grebes can feed, so that, during the breeding season, they can seriously deplete the available food. It is this potential shortage which can lead the adults to put their own survival above that of their chick and abandon it so that they can move to another lake containing more food. Although there are no figures available, it is clear from the very low rate of recruitment that the adult grebes enjoy a very low annual mortality.

When the Hooded Grebes were first discovered, and for nearly 20 years thereafter, their wintering quarters were unknown. Laguna de Los Escarchados was known to freeze over in the winter. Some of the birds collected there had well developed salt glands above their eyes, which made it seem likely that the birds moved to the coast. They had a choice between the nearer, western, side of the South American peninsula among the myriad sheltered fjords on the Chilean coast, and the more distant Atlantic coast of Argentina. The latter seemed more probable, in view of the grebes' preference for feeding in shallow water, and this was finally confirmed in 1994 with the sighting of a flock of 400 birds in the estuary of the Rio Coyle, almost due west of Laguna de Los Escarchados and some 300km (185 miles) south-west of the principal breeding area on the Meseta de Strobel.

Any species with a limited population, a restricted range and particular breeding requirements must be regarded as vulnerable, even though the remoteness and the scattered nature of the breeding lakes makes the Hooded Grebe safer than some. It would take some gross habitat change or, perhaps more likely, an oiling incident in the winter quarters, to affect the population seriously, but in the meantime it can be regarded as pretty secure, despite the small numbers.

Western Grebe

Aechmophorus occidentalis

— NORTHERN RACE *A.o.occidentalis*: Breeds in the western half of the United States and Canada, from the Mexican border north to south-west and southern central Canada, wintering on the Pacific coast from Vancouver south to Baja California and the Gulf of Mexico.

— SOUTHERN RACE *A.o.ephemeralis*: Apparently sedentary; on the Mexican Plateau from northern Chihuahua province to Guerrero province south of Mexico City.

IT IS SPRING AND A PAIR OF WESTERN GREBES ARE displaying to each other. They dip their bills in the water and flick their heads up again, or point their bills at each other with necks held stiffly either straight up or bent at a strange angle. Suddenly, the male whirls to one side, thrusts back with its feet and, lifting itself out of the water, sets off running rapidly across the surface. A fraction of a second later, the female follows suit and the pair rush across the water side by side, heads pointing forward on curved necks and wings held out stiffly to the side. They keep this up for several seconds, covering many metres at high speed, before abruptly subsiding and immediately diving beneath the surface.

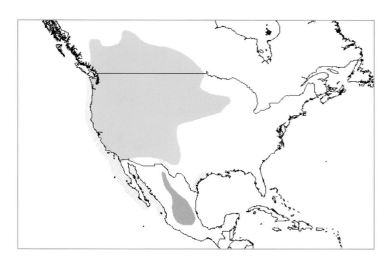

This 'water-dance' of the Western Grebe is among the most spectacular of courtship displays, not just among grebes, but among all birds. It has featured in many films and photographs, though for the full impact it has to be seen in real life. Film, though, has provided the opportunity for a detailed analysis of the display, showing that the birds may travel for up to 20m (65ft) across the water, while their feet patter on the surface at an astonishing 16–20 times a second. What is not always obvious from a film is that this pattering is distinctly audible from considerable distances. The speed of reaction of the second bird, from the time the first one starts rushing to the moment the second one joins it, is also to be marvelled at, taking as it does less than half a second, even as little as a tenth of a second on occasions.

While the description above refers to a pair, in fact the water-dance may be performed by two males, presumably trying to attract an unpaired female in the vicinity. Another variation is a group of one female and two or more males, which could involve the additional males trying to separate the female from its current partner. In many water-dances involving a female and more than one male, the female may stop rushing across the surface before the males, leaving them to carry on further. It is apparent that the birds are not racing each other across the water, because the later-starting bird or birds can always quickly catch up with the first one and then maintain station beside it. One further point of interest is the position of the wings, held stiffly out to the side, but not fully extended. The main flight feathers remain folded and just the innermost feathers, the scapulars, are exposed. It is suggested that this arrangement is important to the birds in maintaining their upright position on the water, providing stability as well as, perhaps, a degree of lift.

While the water-dance as described is carried out in precisely this fashion only by the Western Grebe and the closely related Clark's Grebe, other species may also rush across the water. Horned Grebes, for example, do so while carrying pieces of weed in their bills, though they keep their wings closed. A unique characteristic of Western and Clark's Grebes is the ability to bend the neck in such a way that the bird can stab its head and bill forwards with the

Chris Rose

action of a spear. Although the principal function of this is capturing fish, the birds also make stabbing motions directed towards rivals during courtship.

Like other grebes, the Western has a whole repertoire of courtship displays, often performed in sequence. Researchers studying bird behaviour have invented their own vocabulary for labelling the different displays which, for the most part (though not invariably), give a verbal description of what the birds are doing. Thus, the greeting ceremony of the Western Grebe, which is performed when a well-mated pair come together after a short separation, begins with 'advertising', progresses into 'dip-shaking' and then into 'bob-shaking', which is followed by 'bob-preening' and completed with 'arch-clucking'. Unlike the water-dance, during which the birds are silent, the greeting ceremony is accompanied by specific calls. During advertising, when the birds raise their crests and swim towards each other, both male and female make loud 'cree-creet' calls up to six times in very quick succession, the female's more highly pitched and shorter in duration than the male's. Arch-clucking is characterized by repeated clucking notes, uttered as the bird stretches its neck up straight while keeping its head and bill pointing vertically downwards.

Water-weed plays a significant part in the displays of several species of grebe including the Western. Its weed ceremony often begins with the water-dance, then when the birds have reappeared following their culminating dive, they turn and face each other several metres apart, stretching their necks, raising their crests and cocking their tails. Holding this posture, the birds emit several rapid trills, then move into bob-shaking, dipping their bills and the front of their heads vertically into the water and out again before shaking them to and fro. Next, one of the pair, quickly followed by the other, stretches its neck up before immediately plunging it into the water and dives, sometimes repeatedly, until it finally emerges with a piece of water-weed in its bill. Once both birds are carrying weed, they approach each other, rise up out of the water in a vertical posture, held there by rapidly paddling feet, and point their weed-filled bills upwards at an angle of about 45 degrees. Holding this position about a body's length apart, they stay like that for perhaps 20 seconds, though as long as a minute and a half has been recorded. Then one bird drops the weed with a flick of the head and both birds subside onto the water's surface. The ceremony usually ends with more bob-preening and then arch-clucking.

Not all displays are between the pair. Some are between two males in dispute, one trying to drive the other away if the latter seems to be coming too close to its female or to the nest. Here the dagger-like bill of the grebe is used as a weapon of threat, for example in the graphically described 'ratchet-pointing'. To do this, the bird holds its neck kinked so that the head, with the crest raised, is held low and parallel with the water surface, the bill pointing forward, all the while staring fixedly at its opponent who adopts a similar posture. These staring contests are accompanied by short, harsh calls, like the sound of a ratchet clicking round, and take place with the two birds almost bill-tip to bill-tip, only one or two body-lengths apart. Their aggressive power is clear to see and, as the staring continues, one of the birds can often be seen beginning to move slowly forward while the other retreats backwards in front of it. The display may end with one bird turning tail and diving or in actual physical contact, the birds grasping each other's necks or stabbing with their bills. Actual injury is rare.

The main food of the Western Grebe is fish, sometimes making up virtually 100 per cent of the diet, though the birds also eat aquatic invertebrates. Fish of up to 20cm (8in) are taken, not just by grasping them between the mandibles (the usual manner in which grebes catch their prey), but also by spearing them, especially the deep-bodied species. The grebe uses its unusual ability to extend its neck in a stabbing movement. Although the male and female differ in body size only very slightly, the larger male has a noticeably larger bill, both in length and depth. The significance of this is uncertain and does not seem to be entirely related to differences in diet.

An interesting discovery was made in 1996 concerning the feeding of Western Grebes during the winter. It was observed that the birds were spending nearly all the daytime resting and so were, presumably, feeding at night, though it was not known how they located their prey in the darkness. On breeding waters, the grebes used their eyes to search for prey, often apparently looking for fish prior to diving by dipping their heads as far as the eyes beneath the surface. Capture under water is also by pursuit. Observations with a night scope revealed that the birds on the sea were, indeed, feeding after dark and were doing so by using bioluminescence (sometimes called phosphorescence) in the water to see the tracks made by the fish. The parallel discovery was that the fish they were feeding on were only available at night, as these were species that spend the daylight hours in depths of up to 100m (330ft). The fish come to the surface at night following the zooplankton, which themselves perform a vertical migration both to maximize their opportunities for feeding on phytoplankton and to reduce predation: during the daytime they would be too visible near the surface. The final link in the chain is that the phytoplankton produce the bioluminescence which enables the grebes to 'see' their prey.

In the late 19th and early 20th centuries, Western Grebes suffered, like the Great Crested Grebe in Europe, from the attentions of milliners seeking the soft breast and belly feathers as trimming for 'fur' hats and stoles. Whole colonies were destroyed in some parts of California and Oregon. Threats nowadays come from drainage and pollution of breeding waters and from pollution in the coastal wintering area, where their highly gregarious habits make the grebes especially vulnerable. For example, perhaps as many as 11,000 birds died following an oil spill in San Francisco Bay in January 1971 when over 800,000 gallons was spilt following a collision between two tankers. Western Grebes represented 55 per cent of all the corpses identified.

This single incident may have killed over 10 per cent of the total population of the northern race which is currently estimated at up to 100,000 individuals and, as far as can be told from limited counts, reasonably stable. The much smaller population (less than 10,000) of the southern race in Mexico is of more concern, especially as extensive reed-cutting removes vital nesting habitat at some locations. The fortunes of the Western Grebe remain inextricably linked with those of the less common Clark's Grebe (*see* below).

CLARK'S GREBE

AECHMOPHORUS CLARKII

— NORTHERN RACE *A.c.transitionalis*: Breeds in the western half of the United States from the Mexican border north to Washington and North Dakota and into southern Canada, wintering on the Pacific coast from Vancouver south to Baja California and possibly the Gulf of Mexico.

— SOUTHERN RACE *A.c.clarkii*: Apparently sedentary; on the Mexican Plateau from northern Chihuahua province to Guerrero province south of Mexico City.

CLARK'S GREBE WAS ONLY SEPARATED FROM THE Western Grebe in 1985. For the previous 100 years they were regarded as colour phases of one species, Clark's being the paler of the two, with more white on the wings and flanks. The Western Grebe, as well as being thought to have two colour phases, was further divided into two subspecies, based mainly on size, the larger in the north, breeding in the western United States and Canada, the smaller confined to the Mexican Plateau.

Researchers studying breeding birds in the 1960s and 1970s began to notice that birds of the two colour phases appeared to pair and breed only with birds of their own phase. In two studies at the Bear River Refuge in Utah, totals of 249 pairs of dark-phase birds were recorded, together with 34 pairs of light-phase birds and just five pairs where one parent was dark and the other light phase. This was most unusual, because in studies of other birds where there are different colour phases, for example the Lesser Snow Goose, there is no such assortative mating (as this behaviour is called). A further study, also at Bear River, but extended to take in breeding birds in California and Oregon, looked at much larger samples and found just 14 mixed pairs in 1,185 pairs observed in Utah and only two in more than 600 further pairs seen in California and Oregon. This represents a combined proportion of less than 1 per cent of mixed pairs when, had random mating been taking place, the figure would have been 33 per cent. Some other differences between the dark-phase and light-phase pairs also emerged from this study, including the fact that the two phases appeared to start breeding at different times. It was also noted that the distribution of the two colour phases within colonies and in wintering flocks was not random. Each colour phase appeared to group together more than would be expected by chance.

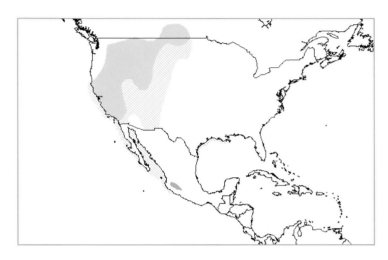

The next stage in what was rapidly turning into a detective story was a study of both dark and light phase birds going through their displays as they paired up in spring. This was carried out at the Klamath Basin refuge on the California-Oregon border where up to 3,000 grebes gathered before dispersing to breed. This study concentrated on both the actual physical displays and the various calls made during them. Although no apparent differences could be found between the two phases in the display movements as the birds courted (or, if there were, they were concealed by the considerable amount of individual variation in the displays), there was a very obvious difference in the main 'advertising' call that the birds utter to attract a mate before they commence their courtship display. The dark-phase birds produced a two-note call, written down as 'cree-creet', while the light-phase birds just called 'creet'. These calls were completely consistent between the two phases. What is more, when the calls were tape-recorded and played back over the water, the courting males of the two phases were readily able to distinguish between them, replying to or swimming towards the correct female call for their

Chris Rose

phase. This difference in calls, combined with, but probably more important than, the differences in colour, are clearly what keeps the two species separate even when they are breeding in the same location.

Further, detailed, work on the birds continued into the early 1980s until, in 1985, the American Ornithologists' Union formally separated the Western Grebe into two species, citing the studies above as the principal evidence for the separation. The following year, it was also acknowledged that, just as there were two distinct subspecies of the Western Grebe, so there were, also, two subspecies of the newly recognized Clark's Grebe. Each species had a larger, northern, race and a smaller, southern one, both 'pairs' of subspecies overlapping to a considerable extent.

Following the recognition of Clark's Grebe as a species in its own right, work started to try to discover its population size and whether it required any conservation management or protection separate from or in addition to that already provided for the Western Grebe. Clark's Grebe is clearly much less numerous than the Western Grebe in the north of the range, with under 1 per cent of birds in Canada and only 12–18 per cent in Utah. However, it is believed to be the commoner of the two in California. Overall, both the northern races of the two species are believed to number somewhere between 50,000 and 100,000 individuals. In Mexico, only rough

estimates are available, but it is believed that while there may be up to 10,000 of the southern race of the Western Grebe, there are under 1,000 of the southern race of Clark's Grebe. If this is confirmed by proposed censuses, it would place it among the rarer grebes.

It has to be said that not everyone agrees with the decision to split the Western Grebe into two species and further studies are continuing, with some concentration on any differences in ecology and breeding biology. As two species do not occupy exactly the same niche throughout the year, it is certain that there will be some differences, although these may be very subtle. When the birds feed, they often do so in mixed flocks, but Clark's Grebes tend to feed slightly further out from the shore than Western Grebes, presumably in deeper water. Diving techniques differ too. Western Grebes prefer to simply slip beneath the surface, while Clark's Grebes leap upwards and out of the water before submerging. This is thought to enable them to dive deeper and thus exploit a slightly different stratum of underwater fish and invertebrates, thereby reducing competition between the two species.

There is clearly more to find out about this newest species of grebe. In the meantime, for all other details of the birds' distribution, behaviour and ecology, in both winter and summer, it is necessary, for now, to refer to accounts of the Western Grebe written before the two species were separated.

91

APPENDIX I
LENGTHS AND WEIGHTS

SPECIES	LENGTH IN CENTIMETRES	WEIGHT IN GRAMS
Little Grebe *Tachybaptus ruficollis*	25–29	130–235
Australasian Grebe *Tachybaptus novaehollandiae*	23–27	100–230
Madagascar Grebe *Tachybaptus pelzelnii*	25	–
Alaotra Grebe *Tachybaptus rufolavatus*	25	–
Least Grebe *Tachybaptus dominicus*	21–27	112–180
Pied-billed Grebe *Podilymbus podiceps*	30–38	340–570
Atitlán Grebe *Podilymbus gigas*	42–52.5	–
White-tufted Grebe *Rollandia rolland*	24–36	–
Titicaca Flightless Grebe *Rollandia microptera*	28–45	–
Hoary-headed Grebe *Poliocephalus poliocephalus*	27–30.5	220–260
New Zealand Grebe *Poliocephalus rufopectus*	28–30	230–270
Great Grebe *Podiceps major*	67–77	c.1,600+
Red-necked Grebe *Podiceps grisegena*	40–55[a]	750–1,600[a]
Great Crested Grebe *Podiceps cristatus*	46–61	600–1,500
Horned Grebe *Podiceps auritus*	31–38	300–570
Black-necked Grebe *Podiceps nigricollis*	28–35	250–600+
Colombian Grebe *Podiceps andinus*	33	–
Silvery Grebe *Podiceps occipitalis*	23–28.5	340–400
Junín Flightless Grebe *Podiceps taczanowskii*	33–38	–
Hooded Grebe *Podiceps gallardoi*	32	–
Western Grebe *Aechmophorus occidentalis*	55–75	800–1,800
Clark's Grebe *Aechmophorus clarkii*	55–75	800–1,800

[a] The Eurasian race is smaller than the North American race, length to 50cm, weight to 900g.
– indicates no data available.

BREEDING DETAILS

THE INFORMATION HERE HAS BEEN GATHERED FROM A number of sources and comes with several qualifications. Where available, the data are expressed as the normal range with extreme ranges shown in parentheses.

Number of broods: The number for a species may vary according to latitude. It should also be noted that where a species is normally single-brooded, some recorded second broods may, in fact, be relayings after a late brood failure.

Clutch size: As is usual with clutch size measurements, the lowest figures may have been incomplete clutches, while the highest may include two females laying in the same nest. Known examples of 'dump' nests, e.g. 25 eggs in a Red-necked Grebe's nest, have been excluded.

Incubation period: The figures given are nearly all approximate as it is often not possible to distinguish whether the published data refer to single eggs or to whole clutches.

Fledging period: Measurements of this only exist for less than half the species, being absent even for an abundant species like the Black-necked Grebe. The habit of this, and some other grebes, of abandoning their young well before fledging adds to the difficulty of determining the period.

SPECIES	BREEDING DISPERSION	NUMBER OF BROODS	CLUTCH SIZE	INCUBATION PERIOD (DAYS)	FLEDGING PERIOD (DAYS)
Little Grebe *Tachybaptus ruficollis*	Territorial	2–3	4 (2–7)	20–25	44–48
Australasian Grebe *Tachybaptus novaehollandiae*	Territorial	2–3	4–5 (1–9)	c.23	c.55
Madagascar Grebe *Tachybaptus pelzelnii*	Territorial	–	3–4	–	–
Alaotra Grebe *Tachybaptus rufolavatus*	Territorial	–	–	–	–
Least Grebe *Tachybaptus dominicus*	Territorial	2–3 (–4)	4–6 (1–10)	c.21	–
Pied-billed Grebe *Podilymbus podiceps*	Territorial	1–2 (–3)	4–7 (1–10)	21–27	35–37
Atitlán Grebe *Podilymbus gigas*	Territorial	–	1–5	–	50+
White-tufted Grebe *Rollandia rolland*	Territorial	2–3	2–3 (1–6)	–	–
Titicaca Flightless Grebe *Rollandia microptera*	Territorial	2–3	2 (1–4)	–	–

93

BREEDING DETAILS

SPECIES	BREEDING DISPERSION	NUMBER OF BROODS	CLUTCH SIZE	INCUBATION PERIOD (DAYS)	FLEDGING PERIOD (DAYS)
Hoary-headed Grebe *Poliocephalus poliocephalus*	Colonial	1	3–5 (1–6)	20–25	–
New Zealand Grebe *Poliocephalus rufopectus*	Territorial	2–3	2–3 (–4)	22–23	c.70
Great Grebe *Podiceps major*	Territorial	2 (–3)	3–5 (2–6)	–	–
Red-necked Grebe *Podiceps grisegena*	Territorial[a]	1 (–2)	4–5 (1–9)	21–33	50–60
Great Crested Grebe *Podiceps cristatus*	Territorial	1 (–2)	3–5 (1–7)	25–31	71–79
Horned Grebe *Podiceps auritus*	Territorial	1 (–2)	4–7 (1–8)	22–25	45–50 (–60)
Black-necked Grebe *Podiceps nigricollis*	Territorial	1 (–2)	2-4 (1–8)	20–23	–[b]
Colombian Grebe *Podiceps andinus*	Territorial	–	–	–	–
Silvery Grebe *Podiceps occipitalis*	Colonial	1	2–4 (1–6)	c.18	–
Junín Flightless Grebe *Podiceps taczanowskii*	Colonial	1	2 (1–3)	–	–
Hooded Grebe *Podiceps gallardoi*	Colonial	1	2	–	–
Western Grebe *Aechmophorus occidentalis*	Colonial	1	3–4 (1–8)	21–28	c.70
Clark's Grebe *Aechmophorus clarkii*	Colonial	1	3–4 (1–7)	c.23	63–77

[a] Occasionally in loose colonies.

[b] Become independent from parents at around 20 days, but fledging period unknown.

STATUS AND CONSERVATION

SPECIES AND SUBSPECIES	DISTRIBUTION	POPULATION	CONSERVATION CATEGORY (*SEE* INTRODUCTION)
Little Grebe			
Tachybaptus ruficollis			Least concern
T.r.ruficollis	Western Palearctic	100,000–1,000,000	Least concern
T.r.iraquensis	Iraq and Iran	c.6,000	Vulnerable
T.r.capensis	Africa, Madagascar, southern Asia	100,000–250,000	Least concern
T.r.poggei	South-east and east Asia	100,000–500,000	Least concern
T.r.philippensis	Philippines	? low thousands	Data deficient
T.r.cotabato	Mindanao, Philippines	? low thousands	Data deficient
T.r.tricolor	Central Indonesia	? low thousands	Data deficient
T.r.vulcanorum	Southern Indonesia	? low thousands	Data deficient
T.r.collaris	New Guinea, Solomon Islands	? low hundreds or thousands	Vulnerable
Australasian Grebe			
Tachybaptus novaehollandiae			Least concern
T.n.novaehollandiae	Australia, New Zealand, New Guinea	c.500,000	Least concern
T.n.leucosternos	Vanuatu and New Caledonia	? low thousands	Vulnerable
T.n.rennellianus	Rennell Island	? low thousands	Vulnerable
T.n.javanicus	Java	? low thousands	Vulnerable
T.n.timorensis	Timor	? low thousands	Vulnerable
T.n.fumosus	Sangihe, Talaud Islands, Indonesia	? low thousands	Vulnerable
T.n.incola	New Guinea	? low thousands	Vulnerable
Madagascar Grebe			
Tachybaptus pelzelnii	Madagascar	5,000–10,000	Vulnerable
Alaotra Grebe			
Tachybaptus rufolavatus	Madagascar	Probably nil	Critically endangered or extinct
Least Grebe			
Tachybaptus dominicus			Least concern
T.d.dominicus	Caribbean	3,000–5,000	Least concern
T.d.brachypterus	Central America	5,000–10,000	Least concern
T.d.bangsi	Baja California, Mexico	5,000–10,000	Least concern
T.d.speciosus	South America	10,000–25,000	Least concern

95

STATUS AND CONSERVATION

SPECIES AND SUBSPECIES	DISTRIBUTION	POPULATION	CONSERVATION CATEGORY (SEE INTRODUCTION)
Pied-billed Grebe			
Podilymbus podiceps			Least concern
P.p.podiceps	North and Central America	hundreds of thousands	Least concern
P.p.antarcticus	South America	10,000–25,000	Least concern
P.p.antillarum	Antilles, West Indies	5,000–10,000	Least concern
Atitlán Grebe			
Podilymbus gigas	Lake Atitlán, Guatemala	0	Extinct
White-tufted Grebe			
Rollandia rolland			Least concern
R.r.rolland	Falkland Islands	1,000–2,000	Data deficient
R.r.chilensis	Southern South America	c.100,000	Least concern
R.r.morrisoni	Lake Junín, Peru	500 and declining	Endangered
Titicaca Flightless Grebe			
Rollandia microptera	Peru and Bolivia	2,000–5,000	Vulnerable
Hoary-headed Grebe			
Poliocephalus poliocephalus	Australia and New Zealand	c.500,000	Least concern
New Zealand Grebe			
Poliocephalus rufopectus	New Zealand	1,200–1,500	Least concern
Great Grebe			
Podiceps major			Least concern
P.m.major	Peru and southern South America	combined total of c.50,000	Least concern
P.m.navasi	Southern Chile	in both subspecies	Least concern
Red-necked Grebe			
Podiceps grisegena			Least concern
P.g.grisegena	Western Palearctic and west Asia	50,000–100,000	Least concern
P.g.holboellii	East Asia and North America	100,000–250,000	Least concern
Great Crested Grebe			
Podiceps cristatus			Least concern
P.c.cristatus	Eurasia	250,000–500,000	Least concern

Status and Conservation

Species and subspecies	Distribution	Population	Conservation category (see Introduction)
P.c.infuscatus	Southern and eastern Africa	5,000–10,000	Data deficient
P.c.australis	Australia and New Zealand	2,500–5,000	Vulnerable
Horned Grebe			
Podiceps auritus			Least concern
P.a.auritus	Eurasia	50,000–100,000	Least concern
P.a.cornutus	North America	100,000–500,000	Least concern
Black-necked Grebe			
Podiceps nigricollis			Least concern
P.n.nigricollis	Eurasia and East Africa	c.150,000	Least concern
P.n.gurneyi	South Africa	25,000–50,000	Data deficient
P.n.californicus	North America	2,000,000–4,000,000	Least concern
Colombian Grebe			
Podiceps andinus	Colombia	0	Extinct
Silvery Grebe			
Podiceps occipitalis			Least concern
P.o.occipitalis	Southern Andes	c.100,000	Least concern
P.o.juninensis	Northern Andes ?	tens of thousands	Least concern
Junín Flightless Grebe			
Podiceps taczanowskii	Lake Junín, Peru	100–200	Critically endangered
Hooded Grebe			
Podiceps gallardoi	Southern Argentina	4,000–5,000	Least concern
Western Grebe			
Aechmophorus occidentalis			Least concern
A.o.occidentalis	North America	c.100,000	Least concern
A.o.ephemeralis	Mexico	5,000–10,000	Vulnerable
Clark's Grebe			
Aechmophorus clarkii			Least concern
A.c.clarkii	Mexico	500–1,000	Vulnerable
A.c.transitionalis	North America	50,000–100,000	Least concern

The information in this table is taken mainly from O'Donnel and Fjeldså (1997) and Rose and Scott (1997). The categories in the final column are those used by the International Union for the Conservation of Nature.

MEANINGS AND DERIVATIONS OF GREBE NAMES

IN THE FOLLOWING LIST, THE MEANINGS OF BOTH English and Latin names are given. The main sources have been Lockwood (1984) and Jobling (1991).

PODICIPEDIDAE

The family name of the grebes is made up of two Latin words *podex* (genitive *podicis*) – the vent or anus, and *pes* – the foot. This describes the structure of all the grebes, with the legs set right at the back of the body.

LITTLE GREBE

'Little' reflects the fact that this is the smallest grebe in Britain. It was first used in conjunction with 'Grebe' in 1768 by Thomas Pennant in his *British Zoology*, vol.2, when he needed to distinguish this species from the Great Crested Grebe. 'Grebe' entered the English language at the same time, when Thomas Pennant adopted it as the name for this whole group of birds. It originally came from a 16th-century French word (*grèbe*) used to mean a gull.

TACHYBAPTUS RUFICOLLIS RUFICOLLIS

Tachybaptus comes from two Greek words, *takhus* – fast, and *baptos* – sinking under or, perhaps, diving. *ruficollis* is from the Latin *rufus* – red and *collis* – neck, and describes the most striking patch of colour on the adult bird.

T.R.IRAQUENSIS

Named for the country of Iraq in which this subspecies occurs.

T.R.CAPENSIS

Refers to the Cape of Good Hope and quite frequently used in bird names to indicate a South African origin or distribution, though this subspecies occurs much more widely, in most of Africa south of the Sahara.

T.R.POGGEI

Poggei refers to Paul Pogge (1838–1884) who has been variously described as an adventurer, a scientist and an African expert. He was born in Mecklenberg, Germany, and spent many years in different parts of Africa, collecting plants and insects. Several of these, including butterflies such as Pogge's Skipper, are named after him. This subspecific name for the Little Grebe was chosen in 1902 by the famous German ornithologist Anton Reichenow (1847–1941), author of important works on German and African birds. He also published a work on the birds of the Bismarck Archipelago in Papua New Guinea, where this subspecies occurs. Through their shared interest in African natural history, Reichenow would have known Pogge and chose this way to honour him.

T.R.PHILIPPENSIS

The obvious name for the subspecies occurring in the Philippines.

T.R.COTABATO

Cotabato is a city on the island of Mindanao in the Philippines to which this subspecies is confined.

T.R.TRICOLOR

Tricolor is straight from the Latin meaning tricoloured, referring to the black, rufous and yellow on the head.

T.R.VULCANORUM

Vulcan was the god of fire in Roman mythology, hence the word 'volcano'. Its use here, in the genitive form, presumably reflects the subspecies' occurrence on the many islands with volcanos, past and present, between Java and Timor, Indonesia.

T.R.COLLARIS

Named by Ernst Mayr in 1945, presumably because there is a trace of a paler collar visible at the base of the dark neck.

AUSTRALASIAN GREBE

Australasia has been defined in a number of different ways. It is frequently taken in political terms to cover just

98

MEANINGS AND DERIVATIONS OF GREBE NAMES

Australia itself, together with New Zealand and other islands of the south-west Pacific, though sometimes also including Papua New Guinea. However, in biogeographic terms, some authors extend the area northwards to take in the whole of New Guinea and its satellite islands, while others state that the true boundary is the Wallace Line which divides the Oriental Region from the Australasian. Wallace found a major faunal discontinuity as he travelled from east to west through Indonesia and placed the islands of Sulawesi and Lombok and islands lying to the east into Australasia, and the islands of Borneo and Bali and those to the west into the Oriental Region.

TACHYBAPTUS NOVAEHOLLANDIAE NOVAEHOLLANDIAE

'New Holland', here Latinized into *novaehollandiae*, was the name given to eastern Australia during the 17th and early 18th centuries. A Dutch sea captain named Willem Janszoon or Jansz was the first European whose claim to having sighted and landed on Australia can be substantiated. He did so in 1606.

T.N.LEUCOSTERNOS

Ernst Mayr was responsible for naming all the subspecies of this grebe. He named two, including this one, which is from the Greek *leukos* – white, *sternon* – the breast, from minor plumage differences, three from their geographical range and one for its sedentary habits. While, despite its name, this subspecies does not actually have a white breast, there is slightly more whitish mottling produced by the white tips of the breast feathers than in the other subspecies.

T.N.RENNELLIANUS

Named for Rennell Island in the Solomon Islands group, where this subspecies occurs. The island in turn was named for the British geographer James Rennell (1742–1830), who was the Surveyor-General of Bengal between 1764 and 1777.

T.N.JAVANICUS

This subspecies occurs on the island of Java, Indonesia.

T.N.TIMORENSIS

This one is found on the island of Timor, also in Indonesia.

T.N.FUMOSUS

The Latin word '*fumos*' means 'smoky', alluding to the plumage difference on which Mayr based his separation of this subspecies, which occurs in the Sangihe and Talaud Islands off Sulawesi, from those on other islands of Indonesia.

T.N.INCOLA

Incola is a Latin word meaning resident. In ornithological terms this could be interpreted as sedentary or non-migratory, reflecting the habits of this subspecies.

MADAGASCAR GREBE

The island of Madagascar, off the west coast of Africa, was discovered in 1500 by a Portuguese expedition. They called the island Ilha de São Lourenço, but early accounts included reports of a tribe of local people variously called the Matacassi, the Madacassa and the Malagasy, this last being one of the languages of the island. The name Madagascar was gradually adopted.

TACHYBAPTUS PELZELNII

There is no doubt that some names are better adapted to Latinization than others! The Austrian ornithologist August von Pelzeln (1825–1891) was curator of the bird and mammal collections in the Imperial Museum of Vienna for over 30 years. During this time he wrote a major work on the birds of Brazil, based on a collection of over 12,000 skins brought back to the museum by a co-worker, and co-authored another on the birds of southern Africa. The grebe was named in his honour by the German ornithologist Gustav Hartlaub (1814–1900) in his treatise on the birds of Madagascar published in 1861.

ALAOTRA GREBE

'Alaotra' is a Malagasy word usually translated as 'the sea'. Lake Alaotra, although freshwater and many miles inland, is much the largest lake in Madagascar so the appellation 'sea' seems very appropriate.

MEANINGS AND DERIVATIONS OF GREBE NAMES

TACHYBAPTUS RUFOLAVATUS

A splendid composite word from the Latin *rufus* – red, and *lavatus* – washed, from *lavare* – to wash or bathe. This grebe's colour is also reflected in one of its alternative English names, Rusty Grebe. A third English name, Delacour's Grebe, honours the French ornithologist Jean Delacour (1890–1985) who first described the bird.

LEAST GREBE

A suitable diminutive for the smallest grebe in the New World, equivalent to the 'Little' of the Old World.

TACHYBAPTUS DOMINICUS DOMINICUS

The name relates to the island now known as Hispaniola, formerly Santo Domingo, the western half of which is the Republic of Haiti, the eastern the Dominican Republic. St Dominic (1170–1221) was a Spanish prior or bishop who founded the Dominican order of friars.

T.D.BRACHYPTERUS

Brachypterus is formed from two Greek words, *brakhus* – short, and *pteros* – winged (from *pterux* – a wing). While the birds of this subspecies, which occurs in central America from southern Texas to Panama, are shorter-winged than the nominate race of the Caribbean, the wings of the next subspecies, of Baja California, are actually slightly shorter still, but this bird was not described as a separate subspecies until many years later.

T.D.BANGSI

Outram Bangs (1863–1932) was curator at the Museum of Comparative Zoology, Harvard, and worked on both birds and mammals, including those of North and Central America. This subspecies, occurring in Baja California, was named in his honour a few years after his death.

T.D.SPECIOSUS

Speciosus is a Latin adjective meaning beautiful, splendid or spectacular, but it is difficult to see why it was chosen for this subspecies of what is, in any case, a decidedly unspectacular grebe. Nearly all the variation between the subspecies is in size, not in plumage.

PIED-BILLED GREBE

'Pied' is used in the sense of marked with black and white, describing the massive whitish bill with the vertical black stripe across it.

PODILYMBUS PODICEPS PODICEPS

In the 18th century, at the time when Linnaeus was compiling his taxonomy, the divers and the grebes were placed in the same genus *Colymbus*, which comes from the Greek *kolumbis* – waterbird. In due course, the divers were separated into *Gavia* and the grebes into *Podiceps*. The latter was then further split and the generic name *Podilymbus* was coined as a hybrid between *Podiceps* and *Colymbus*.

The origin of *podiceps* is described above under the family name Podicipedidae.

P.P.ANTARCTICUS

The word *antarcticus* is used in its correct meaning of 'southern', this subspecies occurring throughout South America and to the south of the other two subspecies.

P.P.ANTILLARUM

Named for the Antilles, islands in the West Indies, the subspecies occurs on both the Greater and Lesser Antilles groups. The name Antilles comes from 'Antilhas', the name given by the Portuguese to Central America.

ATITLÁN GREBE

'Atitlán' aptly translates from the Mayan as 'the place of great water'. This large (130sq km/50 sq miles) lake in Guatemala is also called 'the most beautiful lake in the world'.

PODILYMBUS GIGAS

Gigas is the Latin word for a giant. Other common names for this very large, but sadly now extinct, grebe include Giant Grebe and Giant Pied-billed Grebe.

WHITE-TUFTED GREBE

This is a very suitable name for the only grebe with a tuft of white feathers on its black head.

Meanings and Derivations of Grebe Names

ROLLANDIA ROLLAND ROLLAND

The nominate subspecies is confined to the Falkland Islands. Between 1817 and 1820, the French corvettes *L'Uranie* and *Le Physicienne*, under the command of Louis de Freycinet (1779–1842) circumnavigated the globe with instructions to make observations on geography, ethnology, astronomy, and meteorology, and to collect specimens of flora and fauna. A number of scientists on the expedition included Jean René Quoy and Jean Paul Gaimard. After visiting Australia, the Marianas, Hawaii, and other Pacific islands, de Freycinet lost his ship off the Falkland Islands, where some of the party remained for two months before being brought back to France. The expedition records and collections were saved and de Freycinet subsequently wrote a report of the voyage. The zoological section of the report was written by Quoy and Gaimard, who named this species in honour of M.Rolland, the Master Gunner on *L'Uranie*.

R.R.CHILENSIS

Named for Chile, which is within the range of this widespread South American subspecies.

R.R.MORRISONI

This subspecies is named after Alastair Morrison, who visited Lake Junín in 1938 and collected various birds there whose skins were subsequently deposited in the Natural History Museum in London. He noted at the time that the specimens of White-tufted Grebe from the lake were on average longer in the wing than birds from elsewhere in South America, but did not pursue the matter further. In 1961, the British grebe expert, Ken Simmons, published his view that the birds on Lake Junín deserved subspecific status and named them after Morrison, using one of his skins as the type specimen. In fact, Simmons preferred to treat *Rollandia rolland chilensis* as a separate species, *Podiceps chilensis*, with *morrisoni* as a subspecies, but subsequent authorities have not followed this view. Morrison studied the birds of Peru for several years and himself described and named a number of new species or subspecies.

TITICACA FLIGHTLESS GREBE

The meaning of the word 'Titicaca' remains obscure. A number of possible meanings have been suggested, for example, the stone puma, the rock of the puma or the crag of lead. It is generally agreed that the word is a mixture of two languages, Quechua, the official language of the Inca empire, and an older language, Aymara, both of which are still spoken around the lake and more widely in the mountainous regions of Bolivia, Chile and Peru.

ROLLANDIA MICROPTERA

Microptera is made up of the Greek word *mikros* – small, and *ptera* – winged (as in *brachypterus*, above).

HOARY-HEADED GREBE

As mentioned in the species account, the Hoary-headed Grebe gets its name from the fine silvery-white streaking on its black head.

POLIOCEPHALUS POLIOCEPHALUS

This comes from two Greek words, *polios* – grey and *kephalos* – head.

NEW ZEALAND GREBE

This species is confined to New Zealand.

POLIOCEPHALUS RUFOPECTUS

Rufopectus comes from two Latin words, *rufo* – red and *pectus* – the breast, referring to the reddish colouring of the breast and neck of this species.

GREAT GREBE

'Great' is used in the sense of largest, as this species is of all the grebes.

PODICEPS MAJOR MAJOR

Podiceps, here used as the generic name, is explained above (as the specific name of Pied-billed Grebe). *Major* is Latin and should really be spelt *maior*, which is the comparative form of *magnus*, meaning great. Thus, in English, this is the Great Grebe, but its scientific name translates as 'Greater'.

MEANINGS AND DERIVATIONS OF GREBE NAMES

P.M.NAVASI

This was named as recently as 1984 in honour of an Argentinian ornithologist, Dr Jorge R. Navas, by his co-worker, Maria Manghi.

RED-NECKED GREBE

The name is a good description of the bird, especially in comparison with the Black-necked Grebe (see below). It was first used by Thomas Pennant in his *British Zoology*, vol.2 (1768).

PODICEPS GRISEGENA GRISEGENA

The scientific name describes a different, and less conspicuous, feature of this species by opting for a combination of two Latin words, *griseus* – grey and *gena* – the cheek.

P.G.HOLBOELLII

Carl Peter Holböll (1795–1856) was a Danish zoologist who spent many years in Greenland, travelling widely and collecting specimens for the Copenhagen Zoological Museum. This grebe was named after him in 1854 by Professor J.T. Reinhardt (1816–1882) of Copenhagen University Zoology Department.

GREAT CRESTED GREBE

The use of the word 'great' was introduced in 1768 by Thomas Pennant in his *British Zoology*, vol.2, which also saw the first use of 'little' for Little Grebe (see above). Earlier works had used 'greater' as frequently as 'great', but the former gradually disappeared from the literature.

PODICEPS CRISTATUS CRISTATUS

Cristatus is from the Latin *crista* – a crest.

P.C.INFUSCATUS

The South African subspecies is darker than the nominate, hence *infuscatus* from the Latin *infuscus* – dusky or blackish.

P.C.AUSTRALIS

Australis means 'southern', the Latin root being *auster* – south. The name of Australia, where this subspecies occurs, has the same derivation.

HORNED GREBE

This species has been named for its conspicuous head tufts, or 'horns'. The name is an old one, dating back to at least the middle of the 18th century when George Edwards, in his *A Natural History of Uncommon Birds* (1743–1751), described the 'Horned Dobchick'. Thomas Pennant changed this to Horned Grebe in his *Arctic Zoology* (1785) and while this name is still used in North America it was discarded in Britain in the 19th century firstly by Leonard Jenyns in his *A Manual of British Vertebrate Animals* (1835) and then by William Yarrell in the first edition of his *A History of British Birds* (1837–1843). Both authors used, instead, the name 'Sclavonian Grebe', taking this from George Montagu's *Ornithological Dictionary* (1802). Montagu gave Sclavonian and Horned as alternative names, explaining the first by saying that he had been informed that the species was found in Sclavonia, a name used at that time to describe northern Russia. The spelling was changed to the present 'Slavonian' by Ernst Hartert in his *A Handlist of British Birds* (1912).

In the ongoing discussion on vernacular names of birds, it is perhaps relevant that the name Horned Grebe, far from being some recent North American invention, is in fact the original English name which crossed the Atlantic before 'Sclavonian' came on the scene, and has remained unchanged.

PODICEPS AURITUS AURITUS

Auritus comes from the Latin *auris* – ear, and may be translated as 'eared' or even 'long-eared', a clear reference to the same ear tufts which give the bird its vernacular name.

P.A.CORNUTUS

Cornutus brings us straight back to the vernacular name as it comes from the Latin *cornus* – a horn.

BLACK-NECKED GREBE

'Black-necked' is one of the more recently coined vernacular names. It was first used by Ernst Hartert in his *A Handlist of British Birds* (1912). This replaced the original

MEANINGS AND DERIVATIONS OF GREBE NAMES

name for this species, 'Eared Grebe', in use for the previous 80 years and still used in North America. Hartert was bringing the vernacular name into line with the existing scientific name *nigricollis* (see below). As with Horned/ Slavonian Grebe, the older name has remained unchanged on the other side of the Atlantic and perhaps ought to be given priority in any consideration of a world list of English language vernacular names.

PODICEPS NIGRICOLLIS NIGRICOLLIS

Nigricollis is a straightforward rendering from the Latin *niger* – black, and *collis* – neck.

P.N.GURNEYI

This southern African subspecies was described and named, in 1919, by Austin Roberts (1883–1948), author of the seminal *The Birds of South Africa* (1940). He named it after a father and son, both called John Henry Gurney. The father (1819–1890) was an English banker and member of a famous Norwich family of Quakers. He travelled abroad, including to southern Africa, collecting birds and publishing a number of books and papers. His son (1848–1922) continued the family tradition.

P.N.CALIFORNICUS

The derivation is from the US state of California, the subspecies being described by Adolphus Heermann (1827–1865) who made bird collecting expeditions to a number of different parts of the country. In 1853 he was in California as part of the Pacific Railroad Surveys and published his reports on the birds of that expedition, including this grebe, in 1859. The name 'California' given to the state comes from the name of a fictional earthly paradise in a book called *Las Sergas de Esplanidian*, written by Garcia Ordonez de Montalvo around 1500.

COLOMBIAN GREBE

This species, now extinct, has only ever been recorded from Colombia in north-western South America. The country is, of course, named after Cristobal Colombo, more familiarly known, in English, as Christopher Columbus.

PODICEPS ANDINUS

Named after the Andes mountains, in the Latinized form meaning 'belonging to'. The word 'Andes' is said to be derived from the Quecha word for copper, reflecting the presence of substantial copper deposits.

SILVERY GREBE

'Silvery' is a good descriptive name for this species.

PODICEPS OCCIPITALIS OCCIPITALIS

The specific name comes from the Latin word *occipitium*, meaning the back of the head, which must have attracted the attention of Prosper Garnot (1794–1838), who named it from specimens collected in the Falkland Islands during a voyage round the world, between 1822 and 1825, by the French corvette '*La Coquille*', commanded by Captain Louis Isidore Duperrey. This followed directly after the voyage commanded by Louis de Freycinet (see above under *Rollandia*) and was similarly funded by the French government. Garnot was an assistant surgeon in the French navy, and he collected extensively along the coasts of South America and in the Pacific together with the French naturalist René-Primevère Lesson. Another parallel with the de Freycinet voyage was a shipwreck, which caused the loss of many of Garnot's specimens.

P.O.JUNINENSIS

The subspecific name comes from Lake Junín, Peru, where it occurs.

JUNÍN FLIGHTLESS GREBE

Also named from Lake Junín, Peru.

PODICEPS TACZANOWSKII

The reason for this unusual specific name is explained in the species account.

HOODED GREBE

The name aptly describes the dark head of this species, enlarged by its plumes and contrasting sharply with the whitish neck.

MEANINGS AND DERIVATIONS OF GREBE NAMES

PODICEPS GALLARDOI

This species was discovered as recently as 1974 and named by Maurice Rumboll a noted Argentinian naturalist, at that time collecting birds on behalf of the Argentine Natural History Museum in Buenos Aires. In choosing the name *gallardoi* he managed to celebrate both Angel Gallardo (1867–1934), a very distinguished naturalist and museum director who also served as the government Minister of Education in the 1920s, and later became head of the faculty of natural sciences in the University of Buenos Aires, as well as the local landowners coincidentally also called Gallardo.

WESTERN GREBE

In North America, where this species occurs, the name 'Western' accurately reflects its range.

AECHMOPHORUS OCCIDENTALIS OCCIDENTALIS

Aechmophorus comes from the Greek *aikhmophorus* – a spear carrier (*aikhme* – a spear), referring to the long, thin and pointed bills of these two species. *Occidentalis* matches the vernacular name, coming from the Latin *occidens* – the west.

A.O.EPHEMERALIS

Ephemeralis is from the Greek *ephemeros* – lasting only one day. It was named by the American authority on grebes, Professor Robert Dickerman. He has told me that because the American Ornithologists' Union Committee on Classification and Nomenclature decided to split the former Western Grebe into two species, it became necessary to name the small dark southern population of the Western Grebe and the large pale northern population of the new Clark's Grebe. As Professor Dickerman has expressed some reservations

concerning the split, he chose names that he hoped would be ephemeral!

CLARK'S GREBE

There are two different versions of how this species came to be named. The first is that it was named after William Clark (1770–1838), the explorer who, with Meriwether Lewis, led the celebrated expedition that explored from the Louisiana Territory to the Pacific Coast from 1804 to 1806. The second is that the person was J.H.Clark (1830–?), an American boundary commissioner and a surveyor on the Pacific Railroad Survey, who collected the specimens from which it was named.

The grebe was described, along with the Western Grebe, by George Newbold Lawrence (1806–1895) who worked at the Smithsonian Institution cataloguing the birds collected during surveys for a route for the Pacific Railroad. He described both Clark's and Western Grebes in an account of the birds of North America by Spencer Baird, John Cassin and himself, published in 1858 as one of a series of reports from the Railroad Survey but actually covering all the birds of the whole country. Less than 30 years later, the two species were to be regarded as colour morphs of the Western Grebe and it took a further 100 years before they were once again separated.

AECHMOPHORUS CLARKII CLARKII

Clarkii has the same origin as 'Clark's', above.

A.C.TRANSITIONALIS

Transitionalis from the Latin *transitio* – passage or passing over. This could be taken as reflecting the migratory nature of the subspecies compared with the sedentariness of *A.o.ephemeralis*, but see also the explanation above, of why Professor Dickerman chose *ephemeralis*.

WINTER PLUMAGES

THE DISTINCTIVE BREEDING PLUMAGES OF THE GREBES, with their plumes and crests, give rise to relatively few identification problems. However, this is far from the case during the rather longer period of the year when they are in their non-breeding plumage, and the appearance of all the species can be summed up, as in the Introduction, by 'essentially dark or black above and white below'.

In Europe, the five regular species, Little, Red-necked, Great Crested, Horned and Black-necked, and one vagrant, Pied-billed, can be separated on size and shape as well as plumage differences. The Little lacks any contrasting black and white in its plumage, being mainly drab brown and buff. Although the vagrant Pied-billed also lacks much contrast, it is larger than the Little and its deep and heavy bill is diagnostic.

The Horned and the Black-necked can present identification difficulties in winter, and not just in Europe but in North America too. The former is slightly the larger, with a thicker neck set on a longer body, compared to the rather dumpy Black-necked. Both species have pure white cheeks topped by a sharply contrasting black cap. However, in the Horned, the demarcation line between cheeks and its small cap runs from the bill through the eye. The Black-necked lacks the straight-line divide between the larger black cap on the head and the white cheeks, with a dusky downward protrusion over the ear coverts, which helps form an obvious upward white 'hook' to the rear. The head shape is very different, the Horned having a flattened head, the Black-necked a steep forehead leading to the distinct peak above the eye.

The Great Crested retains its slim elegance in winter, and has a long thin noticeably pale bill. The Red-necked is smaller, though still larger than the Horned, and has buffish cheeks below a darker cap. The bill is distinctly wedge-shaped.

In North America, the Great Crested is replaced by the Western and Clark's. The differences between this pair in winter are very small, with, as shown in the plate, the white on the face of the latter extending above and in front of the eye. Other differences, including a narrower black neck stripe and paler back, show much overlap. Compared with the Red-necked, these two grebes are distinctly larger and more slender. The tiny size of the Least prevents confusion with the Pied-billed.

In addition to some of the North American species, there are a further six species of grebe in Central and South America, plus the extinct Colombian and Atitlán, the latter not being illustrated. The Great certainly lives up to its name, being readily distinguished on size alone. The two flightless grebes, the Junín and the Titicaca, both share their lakes with similar congeners, the White-tufted and Silvery, respectively, with the White-tufted also present on Lake Titicaca, but both are considerably larger in each case so that identification by size comparison is the best way. The Silvery is distinguished from the White-tufted by being overall grey not brown and with much less contrasting crown and cheeks. The winter plumage of the recently discovered Hooded (not illustrated) has yet to be described in full, but it is rather larger than the Silvery and paler on the flanks.

Africa is home to small numbers of Black-necked and Great Crested, neither of which apparently go into winter plumage there, as well as the widespread Little and the two Madagascan endemics, the Madagascar and the Alaotra, though the last-named is probably now extinct. In winter, it was similar to the Little, but with more contrast between crown and cheeks. This is also true of the Madagascar, which further lacks the pale spot at the base of the Little's bill.

There are two confusion species in Australia, the Australasian and the Hoary-headed, to which the New Zealand Grebe must be added in that country. The differences between the first two are fairly subtle, with the demarcation line between dark cap and white cheeks passing through the eye of the Australian but below it in the Hoary-headed, while the latter is also greyer, less buff, on the flanks and rear. It is also a little larger with a heavier head. The New Zealand is more readily distinguished as it lacks the black-and-white contrast on the head, being mainly brown with a darker cap.

AUSTRALASIAN GREBE

LITTLE GREBE

ALAOTRA GREBE

PIED-BILLED GREBE

MADAGASCAR GREBE

LEAST GREBE

WHITE-TUFTED GREBE

TITICACA
FLIGHTLESS
GREBE

HOARY-HEADED GREBE

NEW ZEALAND GREBE

GREAT GREBE

Chris Rose

BLACK-NECKED GREBE

HORNED GREBE

COLOMBIAN GREBE

RED-NECKED GREBE

SILVERY GREBE

GREAT CRESTED GREBE

JUNÍN FLIGHTLESS GREBE

WESTERN GREBE

CLARK'S GREBE

Chris Rose

BIBLIOGRAPHY

THIS LIST CONTAINS ONLY A SELECTION OF THE REFER-
ences used in writing this book, but it does include the
key ones for each species, which will contain many more
useful citations, as well as the major avifaunas used.

Bandorf, H. 1970. *Der Zwergtaucher*. Tachybaptus
ruficollis. Ziemsen, Wittenberg-Lutherstadt.

Boyd, W.S. and Jehl, J.R. Jr. 1998. Estimating the
abundance of Eared Grebes on Mono Lake,
California, by aerial photography. *Colonial Waterbirds*
21: 236–241.

Brown, L.H., Urban, E.K. and Newman, K. 1982. *The
Birds of Africa*, vol.1. Academic Press, London.

Campbell, B. and Lack, E. (eds) 1985. *A Dictionary of
Birds*. Poyser, Calton.

Cramp, S. and Simmons, K.E.L. (eds) 1977. *The Birds of
the Western Palearctic*, vol.1. Oxford University Press,
Oxford.

Cullen, S.A., Jehl, J.R. Jr. and Nuechterlein, G.L.
1999. Eared Grebe (*Podiceps nigricollis*). In: Poole,
A. and Gill, F. (eds) *The Birds of North America*,
No.433. The Birds of North America Inc.,
Philadelphia, PA.

De Smet, K.D. 1987. Organochlorines, predators and
reproductive success of the Red-necked Grebe in
southern Manitoba. *Condor* 89: 460–467.

Dee, T.J. 1986. *The Endemic Birds of Madagascar*. ICBP,
Cambridge.

Del Hoyo, J., Elliott, A and Sargatal, J. 1992. *Handbook of
the Birds of the World*, vol.1. Lynx Edicions, Barcelona.

Dickerman, R.W. 1986. Two hitherto unnamed
populations of *Aechmophorus* (Aves: Podicipitidae).
Proc. Biol. Soc. Wash. 99: 435–436.

Fjeldså, J. 1973. Antagonistic and heterosexual
behaviour of the Horned Grebe, *Podiceps auritus*.
Sterna 12: 161–217.

Fjeldså, J. 1981a. Comparative ecology of Peruvian
grebes – a study of the mechanisms of evolution of
ecological isolation. *Videnskabelige Meddelelser fra
dansk naturhistorisk Forening* 144: 125–249.

Fjeldså, J. 1981b. *Podiceps taczanowskii* (Aves,
Podicipedidae), the endemic grebe of Lake Junín,
Peru: a review. *Steenstrupia* 7: 237–259.

Fjeldså, J. 1982. Some behaviour patterns of four closely
related grebes, *Podiceps nigricollis, P. gallardoi, P.
occipitalis* and *P. taczanowskii*, with reflections on
phylogeny and adaptive aspects of the evolution of
displays. *Dansk Ornithologisk Forenings Tiddskrift* 76:
37–68.

Fjeldså, J. 1983. Social behaviour and displays of the
Hoary-headed Grebe *Poliocephalus poliocephalus*. *Emu*
83: 129–140.

Fjeldså, J. 1985. Displays of the two primitive grebes
Rollandia rolland and *R. microptera* and the origin of
the complex courtship behaviour of the *Podiceps*
species (Aves: Podicipedidae). *Steenstrupia* 11: 133–155.

Fjeldså, J. 1986. Feeding ecology and possible life
history tactics of the Hooded Grebe *Podiceps
gallardoi*. *Ardea* 74: 40–58.

Fjeldså, J. 1988. Comparative ecology of the
Australasian grebes (Aves: Podicipedidae). *Royal
Australian Ornithological Union Report* No.54.

Fjeldså, J. 1993. The decline and probable extinction of
the Colombian Grebe. *Bird Conservation International*
3: 221–234.

Fournier, M.A. and Hines, J.E. 1998. Breeding ecology
and status of the Red-necked Grebe, *Podiceps
grisegena*, in the subarctic of the Northwest
Territories. *Canadian Field-Naturalist* 112: 474–480.

Fox, A.D. 1994. Estuarine winter feeding patterns of
Little Grebes *Tachybaptus ruficollis* in central Wales.
Bird Study 41: 15–24.

Greenquist, E.A. 1982. Displays, vocalisations and
breeding biology of the Great Grebe (*Podiceps major*).
Condor 84: 370–380.

Hajermeijer, W.J.M. and Blair, M.J. 1997. *The EBCC
Atlas of European Breeding Birds*. Poyser, London.

Humphrey, P.S., Bridge, D., Reynolds, P.W. and
Peterson, R.T. 1970. *Birds of Isla Grande (Tierra del
Fuego)*. Preliminary Smithsonian Manual, University
of Kansas Museum of Natural History, Washington,
D.C.

Hunter, L.A. 1988. Status of the endemic Atitlán Grebe
of Guatemala: is it extinct? *Condor* 90: 906–912.

Huxley, J.S. 1914. The courtship-habits of the Great
Crested Grebe (*Podiceps cristatus*) with an addition to

the theory of sexual selection. *Proceedings of the Zoological Society of London* 35: 491–562.

Jehl, J. R., Jr. 1996. Mass mortality events of Eared Grebes in North America. *Journal of Field Ornithology* 67: 471–476.

Jehl, J.R. Jr. 1988. Biology of the Eared Grebe and Wilson's Phalarope in the nonbreeding season: a study of adaptations to saline lakes. *Studies in Avian Biology* 12: 1–74.

Jehl, Jr., J. R. 1997. Cyclical changes in body composition in the annual cycle and migration of the Eared Grebe *Podiceps nigricollis*. *Journal of Avian Biology* 28: 132–142.

Johnsgard, P.A. 1987. *Diving Birds of North America*. University of Nebraska Press, Lincoln, NE.

Jobling, J.A. 1991. *A Dictionary of Scientific Bird Names*. Oxford University Press, Oxford.

LaBastille, A. 1974. Ecology and management of the Atitlán Grebe, Lake Atitlán, Guatemala. *Wildlife Monographs* 37: 1–66.

LaBastille, A. 1992. The Giant Grebes of Atitlán. A chronicle of extinction. *Living Bird Quarterly* 11(1): 10–15.

Langrand, O. 1988. *Guide to the Birds of Madagascar*. Yale University Press, New Haven, CT.

Lockwood, W.B. 1984. *The Oxford Book of British Bird Names*. Oxford University Press, Oxford.

Marchant, S. and Higgins, P.J. (eds) 1990. *Handbook of Australian, New Zealand & Antarctic Birds*, vol. 1, part A. Oxford University Press, Melbourne.

Morony, J.J., Bock, W.J. and Farrand, J. 1975. *Reference List of the Birds of the World*. American Museum of Natural History, New York.

Muller, M.J. and Storer, R.W. 1999. Pied-billed Grebe (*Podilymbus podiceps*). In: Poole, A. and Gill, F. (eds) *The Birds of North America*, No. 410. The Birds of North America Inc., Philadelphia, PA.

Nuechterlein, G.L. 1981. Courtship behavior and reproductive isolation between Western Grebe color morphs. *Auk* 98: 335–349.

Nuechterlein, G.L. and Buitron, D.P. 1989. Diving differences between Western and Clark's Grebes. *Auk* 106: 467–470.

Nuechterlein, G.L. and Storer, R.W. 1982. The pair-formation displays of the Western Grebe. *Condor* 84: 350–369.

Nuechterlein, G.L. and Storer, R.W. 1989. Reverse mounting in grebes. *Condor* 91: 341–346.

O'Donnel, C. and Fjeldså, J. 1997. *Grebes. Status Survey and Conservation Action Plan*. IUCN, Cambridge.

Palmer, R.S. (ed) 1962. *Handbook of North American Birds*, vol.1. Yale University Press, New Haven, CT.

Piersma, T. and van Eerden, M.R. 1989. Feather eating in Great Crested Grebes *Podiceps cristatus*: a unique solution to the problems of debris and gastric parasites in fish-eating birds. *Ibis* 131: 477–486.

Prinzinger, R. 1979. *Der Schwarzhalstaucher* Podiceps nigricollis. Ziemsen, Wittenberg-Lutherstadt.

Ratti, J.T. 1978. Reproductive and isolating mechanisms between sympatric dark- and light-phase Western Grebes. *Auk* 96: 573–586.

Ratti, J.T. 1981. Identification and distribution of Clark's Grebe. *Western Birds* 12: 41–46.

Rose, P.M. and Scott, D.A. 1997. *Waterfowl Population Estimates*, 2nd edn. Wetlands International, Wageningen, The Netherlands.

Selous, E. 1901. An observational diary of the habits – mostly domestic – of the Great Crested Grebe. *The Zoologist* 5: 161–83, 338–50.

Simmons, K.E.L. 1955. Studies on Great Crested Grebes. *Avicultural Magazine* 61: 3–13, 93–102, 131–146, 181–201, 235–253, 294–316.

Simmons, K.E.L. 1962. A new race of the grebe *Podiceps chilensis* from Lake Junín, Peru. *Bull. Brit. Orn. Club* 82: 92–94.

Simmons, K.E.L. 1974. Adaptations in the reproductive biology of the Great Crested Grebe. *British Birds* 67: 413–437.

Simmons, K.E.L. 1997. Brood division, parental favouritism and parental desertion in the Great Crested Grebe. *Bristol Ornithology* 24: 1–61.

Stedman, S.J. 2000. Horned Grebe (*Podiceps auritus*). In: Poole, A. and Gill, F. (eds) *The Birds of North America*, No.505. The Birds of North America Inc., Philadelphia, PA.

Storer, R.W. 1963. Observations on the Great Grebe. *Condor* 65: 279–288.

BIBLIOGRAPHY

Storer, R.W. 1967. Observations on Rolland's Grebe. *Hornero* 10: 339–350.

Storer, R.W. 1969. The behavior of the Horned Grebe in spring. *Condor* 71: 180–205.

Storer, R.W. 1971. The behaviour of the New Zealand dabchick. *Notornis* 18: 175–186.

Storer, R.W. 1980–1981. The Hooded Grebe on Laguna de los Escarchados: ecology and behavior. *Living Bird* 19: 51–67.

Storer, R.W. 1992. Least Grebe (*Tachybaptus dominicus*). In: Poole, A. and Gill, F. (eds) *The Birds of North America*, No.24. The Birds of North America Inc., Philadelphia, PA.

Storer, R.W. and Getty, T. 1985. Geographic variation in the Least Grebe (*Tachybaptus dominicus*). *Ornithological Monographs* 36: 31–39.

Storer, R.W. and Jehl, J.R. Jr. 1985. Moult patterns and moult migration in the Black-necked Grebe *Podiceps nigricollis*. *Ornis Scandinavica* 16: 253–260.

Storer, R.W. and Nuechterlein, G.L. 1985. An analysis of plumage and morphological characters of the two color forms of the Western Grebe (*Aechmophorus*). *Auk* 102: 102–119.

Storer, R.W. and Nuechterlein, G.L. 1992. Western and Clark's Grebe (*Aechmophorus occidentalis* and *A. clarkii*). In: Poole, A. and Gill, F. (eds) *The Birds of North America*, No.26. The Birds of North America Inc., Philadelphia, PA.

Stout, B.E. and Nuechterlein, G.L. 1999. Red-necked Grebe (*Podiceps grisegena*). In: Poole, A. and Gill, F. (eds) *The Birds of North America*, No.465. The Birds of North America Inc., Philadelphia, PA.

Ulenaers, P. and Dhondt, A.A. 1994. Great Crested Grebe *Podiceps cristatus* chick mortality in relation to parental fishing. *Bird Study* 41: 211–220.

Ulenaers, P., van Vessem, J. and Dhondt, A.A. 1992. Foraging of the Great Crested Grebe in relation to food supply. *Journal of Animal Ecology* 61: 659–667.

Vlug, J.J. and Fjeldså, J. 1990. *Working Bibliography of Grebes of the World*. Zoological Museum, University of Copenhagen, Copenhagen.

Wilmé, L. 1994. Status, distribution and conservation of two Madagascar bird species endemic to Lake Alaotra: Delacour's grebe *Tachybaptus rufolavatus* and Madagascar pochard *Aythya innotata*. *Biological Conservation* 69: 15–21.

INDEX

The figures in **bold** after each species' name indicate the page numbers of the main account, including the distribution map, and the plates.

INDEX

112